Important Instruction

Students, Parents, and Teachers can use the URL or QR code provided below to access hundreds of additional practice questions, educational videos, worksheets, mobile apps, standards information and more.

URL	QR Code
Visit the URL below and place the book access code **http://www.lumoslearning.com/a/tedbooks** **Access Code: LSMG2M-74285-P**	

lumos learning
Developed by Expert Teachers

Lumos Skills Mastery tedBook - Grade 2 Math: Standards-based Mathematics practice workbook

Contributing Author	-	**Amber Williams**
Contributing Author	-	**Mary Waters Cox**
Executive Producer	-	**Mukunda Krishnaswamy**
Database Administrator	-	**R. Raghavendra Rao**
Designer & Illustrator	-	**Sowmya R.**

First Edition - 2020

NGA Center/CCSSO are the sole owners and developers of the Common Core State Standards, which does not sponsor or endorse this product. © Copyright 2010. National Governors Association Center for Best Practices and Council of Chief State School Officers.

ISBN-10: 1-946795-98-4

ISBN-13: 978-1-946795-98-4

Printed in the United States of America

For permissions and additional information contact:

Lumos Information Services, LLC
PO Box 1575, Piscataway, NJ 08855-1575
http://www.LumosLearning.com

Email: support@lumoslearning.com
Tel: (732) 384-0146
Fax: (866) 283-6471

Lumos Learning
Developed by Expert Teachers

Table of Contents

Online Program Benefits

Students*

- Rigorous Standards Practice
- Technology-enhanced item types practice
- Additional learning resources such as videos and apps

Parents*

- You can review your student's online work by login to your parent account
- Pinpoint student areas of difficulty
- Develop custom lessons & assignments
- Access to High-Quality Question Bank

Teachers*

- Review the online work of your students
- Get insightful student reports
- Discover standards aligned videos, apps and books through EdSearch
- Easily access standards information along with the Coherence Map
- Create and share information about your classroom or school events

* Terms and Conditions apply

URL	QR Code
Visit the URL below and place the book access code **http://www.lumoslearning.com/a/tedbooks** **Access Code: LSMG2M-74285-P**	

Start using the online resources included with this book today!

Introduction

This book is designed to provide rigorous standards-aligned skills practice to second grade students. Students will obtain a better understanding of each standard and improve on their weaknesses by practicing the questions provided in this workbook. The lessons contain rigorous questions aligned to the state standards and substandards. Taking the time to work through the activities will afford students the ability to become proficient in each grade level standard.

Unlike a traditional book, this Lumos tedBook offers Online access to additional learning resources and more practice questions. Practicing the questions provided in these digital workbooks will not only help students get a comprehensive review of standards, but also become familiar with the technology enhanced question types.

Why Practice by Standard?

Each standard and substandard has its own specific learning objectives. Taking the time to study and practice each standard individually will create opportunities for students to master those learning objectives and demonstrate proficiency. Additionally, students have individual strengths and weaknesses. Being able to practice content by standard allows them to efficiently strengthen areas of their weaknesses.

How Can the Lumos Study Program Prepare Students for Standardized Tests?

Student's mastery of the State Standards are being assessed using standardized testing methods. At Lumos Learning, we believe that yearlong learning and adequate practice before the actual test are the keys to success on these standardized tests. We have designed this book to help students learn each standard through engaging videos and other resources and practice using questions provided in the book and Online.

What is Lumos tedBook™?

Lumos tedBook™ connects practice questions provided in this printed workbook with engaging Online resources. These additional resources can be accessed using a number of devices including Android phones, iPhones, tablets and personal computers. Each Online Workbook will have some of the same questions seen in this printed book, along with additional questions, apps and videos. Students will get instant feedback and can review their answers anytime. Each student's answers and progress can be reviewed by parents and educators to reinforce the learning experience.

Discover Engaging and Relevant Learning Resources

Lumos EdSearch is a safe search engine specifically designed for teachers and students. Using EdSearch, you can easily find thousands of standards-aligned learning resources such as questions, videos, lessons, worksheets and apps. Teachers can use EdSearch to create custom resource kits to perfectly match their lesson objective and assign them to one or more students in their classroom.

To access the EdSearch tool, use the search box after you log into Lumos StepUp or use the link provided below.

http://www.lumoslearning.com/a/edsearchb	

The Lumos Standards Coherence map provides information about previous level, next level and related standards. It helps educators and students visually explore learning standards. It's an effective tool to help students progress through the learning objectives. Teachers can use this tool to develop their own pacing charts and lesson plans. Educators can also use the coherence map to get deep insights into why a student is struggling in a specific learning objective.

Teachers can access the Coherence maps after logging into the StepUp Teacher Portal or use the link provided below.

http://www.lumoslearning.com/a/coherence-map	

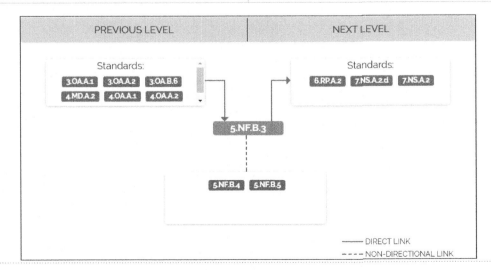

How to use this book effectively

The Lumos Program is a flexible learning tool. It can be adapted to suit a student's skill level and the time available to practice before standardized tests. Here are some tips to help you use this book and the Online resources effectively:

Students

- The standards in each book can be practiced in the order designed, or in the order you prefer.
- Complete all problems in each workbook.
- Use the Online Workbooks to further practice your areas of difficulty and as a way to complement classroom learning.
- Download the Lumos StepUp® app using the instructions provided in Lumos StepUp® Mobile App FAQ For Students to have access to Online resources anywhere you go.

Parents

- Help your child use Lumos StepUp® Online Workbooks by following the instructions provided in "Access Online Program" section.
- You can review your student's online work by login to your parent account.
- You can also conveniently access student progress report on your mobile devices by downloading the Lumos StepUp app. Please follow directions provided in the "How can I Download the App?" section in Lumos StepUp® Mobile App FAQ For Parents and Teachers.

Chapter 1:
Operations and Algebraic Thinking

Lesson 1: Solve Addition And Subtraction Problems

You can scan the QR code given below or use the url to access additional EdSearch resources including videos and mobile apps related to *Solve Addition And Subtraction Problems*.

Filters   Clear All Filters   About 27 results (0.146 seconds)

Grades ⌃

☐ 3 ☐ 4 ☐ 5 ☐ 6 ☐ 7

☐ 8 ☐ 9 ☐ 10 ☐ 11 ☐ 12

Subjects ⌃

☑ Math   ☐ ELA

Find the missing number (addition and subtraction within 100)

Missing numbers within 100
Khan Academy

Resource: Videos

Learn how to solve missing number problems like 73 = ___ + 57.

★ ★ ★ ★ ★ ▾

---

ed)Search   **Solve Addition And Subtraction Problems**

URL	QR Code
http://www.lumoslearning.com/a/2oaa1	

---

1. **Linda has 71 pages in her book. She read 23 pages. How many more pages does Linda have left to read?**

   Ⓐ 52
   Ⓑ 94
   Ⓒ 58
   Ⓓ 48

2. **Kim has 24 pieces of candy left after she gave 17 pieces to her classmate. How many pieces of candy did Kim have at first?**

   Ⓐ 41
   Ⓑ 7
   Ⓒ 13
   Ⓓ 31

3. **Lucy had 14 dollars and her father gave her 26. She went and bought an art kit for 15 dollars. How many dollars does Lucy have now?**

   Ⓐ 40
   Ⓑ 25
   Ⓒ 9
   Ⓓ 55

4. **Brad ate 11 grapes out of the bag. Jay ate 14 grapes out of the bag. If there are 43 grapes still in the bag, how many grapes were in the bag at first?**

   Ⓐ 3
   Ⓑ 25
   Ⓒ 18
   Ⓓ 68

5. **Jimmy exercised for 36 minutes on Monday. He exercised for 12 more minutes on Tuesday, than he did on Monday. How many minutes did Jimmy exercise in all for both Monday and Tuesday?**

   Ⓐ 48
   Ⓑ 24
   Ⓒ 38
   Ⓓ 84

6. Mark earned a 98 on his Math quiz this week. He earned 11 points higher this week than he earned on his quiz last week. What grade did Mark earn on last week's quiz?

7. Put a check mark under the correct equation to solve each word problem.

	34+17=?	34−17=?
Lisa had 34 books. She read 17. How many books did she not read?		
Lisa bought 17 books. She had 34. How many books does Lisa have now?		

8. Brittney and Joshua are saving their money to buy a new video game for $59. Brittney has $26 saved and Joshua has $19 saved. Answer below questions.

How much money have Brittney and Joshua saved altogether?	
How much more money does Brittney have saved than Joshua?	
How much more money do they need to save to buy the video game?	

9. Kevin and Chia are watching a game show. Player A has 47 points. Player B has 32 points. Kevin says Player B needs to earn 79 points to catch up with Player A. Chia says Player B only needs to earn 15 points to catch up to Player A. Who is correct? Kevin or Chia? Explain.

10. John had 23 stickers. Lisa had 14 stickers. Which equation can be used to find out how many more stickers John had than Lisa?

  Ⓐ 23 + 14=37
  Ⓑ 23 - 14=9
  Ⓒ 37 - 14=23
  Ⓓ 14 + 23=37

Chapter 1

Lesson 2: Addition And Subtraction Problems

You can scan the QR code given below or use the url to access additional EdSearch resources including videos and mobile apps related to *Addition And Subtraction Problems*.

 **Addition And Subtraction Problems**

URL	QR Code
http://www.lumoslearning.com/a/2oab2	

1. Select TWO equations that equal the same sum.

  Ⓐ   12 + 4 = ?
  Ⓑ   12 + 2 = ?
  Ⓒ   3 + 13 = ?
  Ⓓ   4 + 14 = ?

2. Choose TWO equations that equal the same difference.

  Ⓐ   19 - 4 = ?
  Ⓑ   15 - 8 = ?
  Ⓒ   17 - 7 = ?
  Ⓓ   20 - 13 = ?

3. Select TWO equations that would equal the same number.

  Ⓐ   12 - 8 = ?
  Ⓑ   14 - 2 = ?
  Ⓒ   9 + 3 = ?
  Ⓓ   15 + 3 = ?

4. Select all of the equations that have a sum of 20.

  Ⓐ   13 + 7 = ?
  Ⓑ   8 + 12 = ?
  Ⓒ   1 + 19 = ?
  Ⓓ   4 + 6 = ?
  Ⓔ   10 + 10 = ?

5. Select all of the equations that have a difference of 4.

  Ⓐ   17 - 4 = ?
  Ⓑ   12 - 8 = ?
  Ⓒ   19 - 15 = ?
  Ⓓ   20 - 5 = ?
  Ⓔ   10 - 6 = ?

6. What number added to itself equals 14?

  ┌─────────────────────────────┐
  │   │
  │   │
  └─────────────────────────────┘

7. Place a check mark under the correct column to tell whether the equation equals 12 or does not equal 12.

	Equals 12	Does not Equal 12
14 + 3=?		
11 + 1=?		
20 - 8=?		
18 - 6=?		
2 + 10=?		

8. Complete the table by filling in the missing number in each equation.

15	+		=	17
19	-	7	=	
	+	5	=	7
18	-		=	3

9. Carl had 9 stickers left after he gave his best friend some. Write an equation and statement that could represent how many stickers Carl had at first and how many he gave away. Explain.

10. Select all of the equations that equals 11.

Ⓐ 15 - 4=?
Ⓑ 7 + 5=?
Ⓒ 20 - 11=?
Ⓓ 9 + 2=?

Chapter 1

Lesson 3: Groups Of Odd And Even Numbers

You can scan the QR code given below or use the url to access additional EdSearch resources including videos and mobile apps related to *Groups Of Odd And Even Numbers*.

 **Groups Of Odd And Even Numbers**

URL	QR Code
http://www.lumoslearning.com/a/2oac3	

1. **Which number below is an even number?**

   Ⓐ 28
   Ⓑ 13
   Ⓒ 11
   Ⓓ 17

2. **Select the equation that equals an even number.**

   Ⓐ 4+7=?
   Ⓑ 3+2=?
   Ⓒ 6+6=?
   Ⓓ 4+5=?

3. **Select the equation that equals an odd number.**

   Ⓐ 3+3=?
   Ⓑ 10+10=?
   Ⓒ 4+8=?
   Ⓓ 3+6=?

4. **James has an odd number of socks in his drawers. Choose the number below that could be the number of socks that James has.**

   Ⓐ 22
   Ⓑ 48
   Ⓒ 17
   Ⓓ 30

5. **Select all of the numbers that are even.**

   Ⓐ 61
   Ⓑ 89
   Ⓒ 98
   Ⓓ 16
   Ⓔ 24

6. Choose all of the equations that will equal an odd number.

Ⓐ 5+6=?
Ⓑ 3+7=?
Ⓒ 8+10=?
Ⓓ 4+3=?
Ⓔ 9+2=?

7. In her drawer, Carrie has 9 pairs of socks and 1 sock she could not find a match for. How many socks does Carrie have in her drawer?

8. Choose if each group of circle represents an even or odd number.

	EVEN	ODD
OOOOOOO OOOOOO		
OOOOOOOO OOOOOOOO		
OOOO + OOO = ?		
OO + OOOO = ?		

9. Complete the table using the words even and odd.

EVEN	+		=	ODD
ODD	+	ODD	=	
	-	EVEN	=	EVEN

10. Mrs. Drew has 11 boys and 13 girls in her class. She wants all of her students to get in pairs to play a Math game. Is that possible? Show your work and explain your answer.

Chapter 1

Lesson 4: Addition Using Rectangular Arrays

You can scan the QR code given below or use the url to access additional EdSearch resources including videos and mobile apps related to *Addition Using Rectangular Arrays*.

 Search

Addition Using Rectangular Arrays

URL	QR Code
http://www.lumoslearning.com/a/2oac4	

1. Choose the addition equation that represents the array.

OOOOO
OOOOO
OOOOO

Ⓐ 3+3+3=?
Ⓑ 5+5+5+5+5=?
Ⓒ 5+5+5=?
Ⓓ 3+5=?

2. Choose the addition equation that represents the array.

OOOO
OOOO
OOOO
OOOO
OOOO

Ⓐ 4+4+4+4+4=?
Ⓑ 5+5+5+5+5=?
Ⓒ 5+4=?
Ⓓ 4+4+5+5=?

3. Choose the addition equation that represents the array.

OO
OO
OO
OO
OO
OO

Ⓐ 2+2+6+6+6+6=?
Ⓑ 2+2+2+2+2+2=?
Ⓒ 6+2=?
Ⓓ 6+6+6+6+6+6=?

4. Select the array that equals 12.

Ⓐ
```
OOOO
OOOO
OOOO
```

Ⓑ
```
OOOO
OOOO
```

Ⓒ
```
OOOO
OOOO
OOOO
OOOO
```

Ⓓ
```
OOO
OOO
OOO
```

5. Select TWO equations that are represented by the array.

```
OOOOO
OOOOO
OOOOO
```

Ⓐ $5+5+5=?$
Ⓑ $3 \times 5=?$
Ⓒ $3+3+3=?$
Ⓓ $3 \times 3=?$

6. Select TWO equations that are represented by the array.

Ⓐ 5×2=?
Ⓑ 5+5+5+5+5=?
Ⓒ 2×2=?
Ⓓ 2+2+2+2+2=?

7. At band practice, there are 5 rows and 4 students in each row. How many students are at band practice?

8. Match each array to one of the sums by placing a check mark under the correct column.

	12	18
OOO OOO OOO OOO		
OOOOOOOOO OOOOOOOOO		
OOOO OOOO OOOO		
OOOOOO OOOOOO OOOOOO		

9. Tiffany has books arranged onto 3 shelves and 8 books on each shelf. Draw an array with a matching addition equation that represents Tiffany's books. How many books does Tiffany have in all? Explain your answer.

10. Complete the table by filling in the array, addition equation, and/or multiplication equation.

ARRAY	ADDITION EQUATION:	MULTIPLICATION EQUATION:
OOOO OOOO	4 + 4 = ?	
	3 + 3 + 3 = ?	3 X 3 = ?
OO OO OO OO OO		5 X 2 = ?
	5 + 5 + 5 = ?	

Chapter 1:
Operations and Algebraic Thinking
Answer Key
&
Detailed Explanations

Lesson 1: Solve Addition And Subtraction Problems

Question No.	Answer	Detailed Explanations
1	D	The answer is D. 71 pages are the total and a part to subtract is 23 pages. 71 minus 23 is 48.
2	A	The answer is A. If Kim has 24 pieces after she gave 17 away, then you must add the numbers to find out how much she had before giving any away. 24 plus 17 equals 41.
3	B	The answer is B. Lucy had 14 and her father gave her 26, so you should add those numbers together. 14 plus 26 equals 40. She went and bought an art kit for 15 dollars, so you should subtract to show that money being taken away. 40 minus 15 equals 25.
4	D	The answer is D. There are 43 grapes in the bag, in order to find out how many were in there at first you have to add what was taken out. 43 plus 11 (Brad) plus 14 (Jay) equals 68.
5	D	The answer is D. Jimmy exercised for 36 minutes on Monday. To find out how long he exercised on Tuesday, you must add 36 and 12. 36 plus 12 equals 48. 36 (Monday) plus 48 (Tuesday) equals 84.
6	87	The answer is 87. You are finding the difference between the grade this week and last week. To find a difference, you must subtract. 98 minus 11 equals 87.
7		The first problem should be solved using subtraction because you are taking away the books read to find out the books that have not been read. The second problem is solved using addition because you are adding the books Lisa bought to the books she already had.
8		26 plus 19 equals 45, so that is the amount that Brittney and Joshua have saved. You should subtract to find the difference between the money Brittney has saved and Joshua has saved. The difference between 26 and 19 is 7. The video game costs 59 dollars and they already have 45. You should subtract to find out how much more money they need to buy the game. 59 minus 45 equals 14.
9		Chia is correct because in order to find out how many more Player B needs, you have to find the difference between Player A and Player B points. To find a difference you must subtract. 47 – 32 equals 15, so that is why Chia is correct.
10	B	The answer is B. When comparing, you subtract to find the difference between numbers. If John had 23 and Lisa had 14, then John had 9 more stickers than Lisa.

Lesson 2: Addition And Subtraction Problems

Question No.	Answer	Detailed Explanations
1	A & C	The answers are A and C, because they both equal 16 when added together.
2	B & D	The answers are B & D, because they both equal 7 when subtracted.
3	B & C	The answers are B & C. The difference of 14 minus 2 is 12. The sum of 9 plus 3 is 12.
4	A, B, C & E	The answers are A, B, C, and E, because they all equal 20 when the addends are added together.
5	B, C & E	The answer are B, C, & E , because they all equal 4 when they are subtracted.
6	7	The answer is 7. $7 + 7 = 14$.
7		$14 + 3 = 17$ Does not equal to 12 $11 + 1 = 12$ Equals to 12 $20 - 8 = 12$ Equals to 12 $18 - 6 = 12$ Equals to 12 $2 + 10 = 12$ Equals to 12
8		$15 + \mathbf{2} = 17$ $19 - 7 = \mathbf{12}$ $\mathbf{2} + 5 = 7$ $18 - \mathbf{15} = 3$
9		$19 - 10 = 9$. Carl could have had 19 and could have given his friend 10 and he would have 9 stickers left because 19 minus 10 equals 9.
10	A & D	The answers are A & D, because when 4 is subtracted from 15 it equals 11. When 9 is added to 2, it equals 11.

Lesson 3: Groups Of Odd And Even Numbers

Question No.	Answer	Detailed Explanations
1	A	The answer is A. Even numbers are numbers that are divisible by 2. Even numbers have 0,2,4,6,8 in the ones place.
2	C	The answer is C. 6 plus 6 equals 12 and 12 is an even number. Two even numbers will always equal an even number. Two odd numbers will always equal an even number. An equal and an odd number will always equal an odd number.
3	D	The answer is D. 3 plus 6 equals 9 and 9 is an odd number. An even and an odd number will always equal an odd number. Two even numbers will always equal an even number. Two odd numbers will always equal an odd number.
4	C	The answer choice C is correct. 22, 48, and 30 are all even numbers and 17 is the only odd number in the choices given. Hence, 17 could be the number of socks that James has.
5	C, D & E	The answer are C, D, & E. Even numbers have the digit 0, 2, 4, 6 or 8 in the ones place.
6	A, D & E	The answer are A, D, & E. An even and an odd number will always equal an odd number. Two even numbers will always equal and even number. Two odd numbers will always equal an odd number.
7	19	The answer is 19. You can draw out 9 pairs and one additional. When you count the 9 pairs you get 18 and when you add one more you get 19. It should be understood the answer will be an odd number because they are not all paired (Divisible by 2).
8	Odd Even Odd Even	13 (7+6) is odd, 16 (8+8) is even, 7 (4+3) is odd, 6 (2+4) is even. Even numbers are divisible by two and always has a pair. Odd numbers have visually have one left over.
9	Odd Even Even	An even and an odd number will always equal an odd number. Two odd numbers will always equal an even number. Two even numbers will always equal an even number.
10	Yes	Yes, it is possible for all of Mrs. Drew's students to get in pairs. Mrs. Drew has 24 students. 24 students is an even number, so everyone can have a partner. There will be 12 pairs.

Lesson 4: Addition Using Rectangular Arrays

Question No.	Answer	Detailed Explanations
1	C	The answer is C. There are 3 rows and 5 circles in each row. You should add 5 three times.
2	A	The answer is A. There are 5 rows and 4 circles in each row. You should add 4 five times.
3	B	The answer is B. There are 6 rows and 2 circles in each row. You should add 2 six times.
4	A	The answer is A. $4 + 4 + 4 = 12$.
5	A & B	The answers are A & B. The arrays can be represented as an addition equation by adding the number of circles in the row (5) as many times as there are rows (3). The array can also be represented by multiplying the number of rows (3) by how many circles are in each row (5).
6	A & D	The answers are A & D. The arrays can be represented as an addition equation by adding the number of circles in the row (2) as many times as there are rows (5). The array can also be represented by multiplying the number of rows (5) by how many circles are in each row (2).
7	20	The answer is 20. You should draw an array of 5 rows and 4 in each row. You can use an addition sentence $4 + 4 + 4 + 4 + 4 = 20$.
8		The answers can be found by using addition equations, multiplication equations, and/or counting.
9		$8 + 8 + 8 = 24$ Tiffany has 24 books. There are 3 shelves and 8 books on each shelf. I used repeated addition to add 8 three times and got the answer 24.

10		1. Multiplication Equation: $2 \times 4 = ?$
		2. OOO
		   OOO
		   OOO
		3. Addition Equation is: $2 + 2 + 2 + 2 + 2 = ?$
		4. OOO
		   OOO
		   OOO
		   OOO
		   OOO

Chapter 2:
Number & Operations in Base Ten

Lesson 1: Three Digit Numbers

You can scan the QR code given below or use the url to access additional EdSearch resources including videos and mobile apps related to *Three Digit Numbers*.

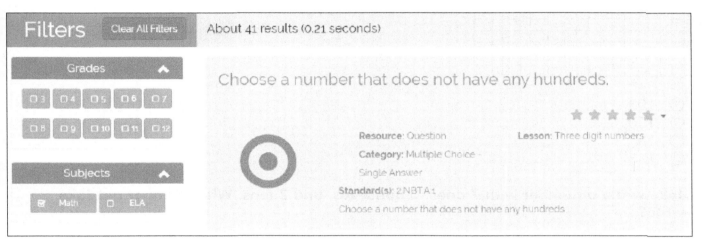

Three Digit Numbers

URL	QR Code
http://www.lumoslearning.com/a/2nbta1	

1. Which number has 4 hundreds, 3 ones, and 2 tens?

   Ⓐ 432
   Ⓑ 234
   Ⓒ 423
   Ⓓ 342

2. Which number is represented by the place value blocks?

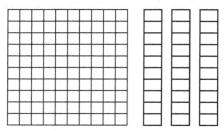

   Ⓐ 103
   Ⓑ 130
   Ⓒ 13
   Ⓓ 133

3. Jake wrote a number with 7 ones, 3 hundreds, and 2 tens. What number did Jake write?

   Ⓐ 327
   Ⓑ 372
   Ⓒ 732
   Ⓓ 237

4. Select the number that has 6 tens, 8 ones, and 5 hundreds.

   Ⓐ 685
   Ⓑ 586
   Ⓒ 856
   Ⓓ 568

5. Choose a number that does not have any hundreds.

   Ⓐ 300
   Ⓑ 58
   Ⓒ 700
   Ⓓ 900

6. Choose a number that does not have any ones.

Ⓐ 809
Ⓑ 340
Ⓒ 209
Ⓓ 33

7. How many tens are bundled to make one hundred?

8. Place a check mark under each column of the correct number.

	583	385	853	538
8 ones, 3 tens, 5 hundreds				
8 hundreds, 5 tens, 3 ones				
8 tens, 3 ones, 5 hundreds				
5 ones, 3 hundreds, 8 tens				

9. Complete the table by filling in the missing columns on each row.

ONES	HUNDREDS	TENS	NUMBER
8	4	5	
7	0		37
			974

10. Sam wrote a number that has 4 ones and 15 tens. Is Sam's number a two-digit or three-digit number? What number did Sam write? Illustrate and explain your answer.

Chapter 2

Lesson 2: Count In Hundreds

You can scan the QR code given below or use the url to access additional EdSearch resources including videos and mobile apps related to *Count In Hundreds.*

 **Count In Hundreds**

URL	QR Code
http://www.lumoslearning.com/a/2nbta1b	

1. There are 5 hundreds below. How many tens are there?

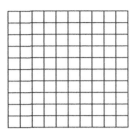 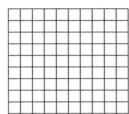 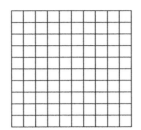 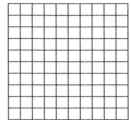 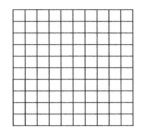

Ⓐ   50
Ⓑ   5
Ⓒ   500
Ⓓ   55

2. How many groups of 100 are below?

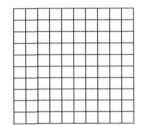 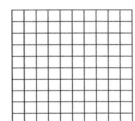 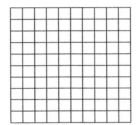

Ⓐ   30
Ⓑ   3
Ⓒ   300
Ⓓ   33

3. How many ones are shown below?

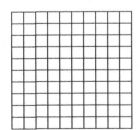 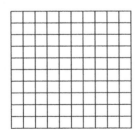

Ⓐ   20
Ⓑ   2
Ⓒ   200
Ⓓ   22

4. Which group shows 400?

Ⓐ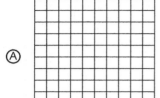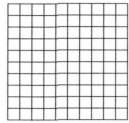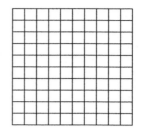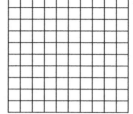

Ⓑ

Ⓒ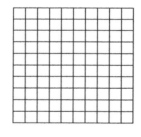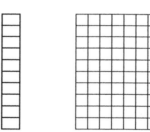

Ⓓ

5. 80 tens equals how many hundreds?

Ⓐ 80
Ⓑ 8
Ⓒ 800
Ⓓ 88

6. How many groups of hundred can be made from the blocks below?

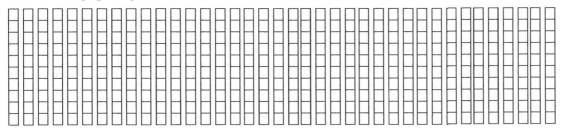

Ⓐ 300
Ⓑ 30
Ⓒ 3
Ⓓ 380

7. Josh drew 6 hundred base-blocks and 10 ten base-blocks. How many hundreds did Josh's drawing represent?

8. Blake said that 700 ones is more than 70 tens. Is he correct? Explain your answer.

LumosLearning.com

9. Match each group of blocks to the number of hundreds you can make. All numbers might not be checked.

	2	3	6

LumosLearning.com

10. Complete the table by filling in each row.

Image
1

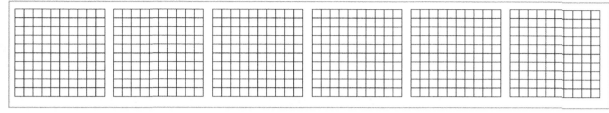

Image
2

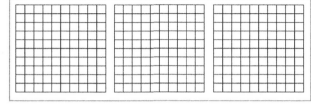

Image
3

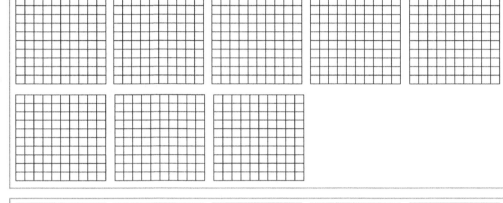

Image
4

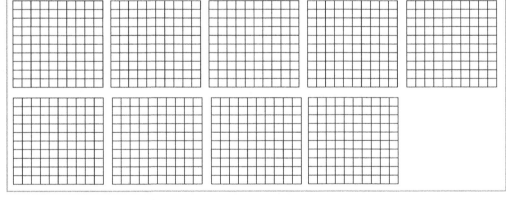

IMAGE	Hundreds	Tens	Ones
1	6	60	
2		30	300
3	8		
4			

Chapter 2

Lesson 3: Count Within 1000

You can scan the QR code given below or use the url to access additional EdSearch resources including videos and mobile apps related to *Count Within 1000*.

 **Count Within 1000**

URL	QR Code
http://www.lumoslearning.com/a/2nbta2	

1. What number goes in the blank?
   235, 240, 245, 250, ____

Ⓐ 5
Ⓑ 250
Ⓒ 260
Ⓓ 255

2. What is the missing number?
   200, ____, 400, 500

Ⓐ 300
Ⓑ 250
Ⓒ 600
Ⓓ 210

3. Start at 67 and count up by tens. What is the 4th number?
   67, ___, ____, ____, ?

Ⓐ 77
Ⓑ 97
Ⓒ 467
Ⓓ 107

4. Select all of the numbers you would say if you were counting by 5's from 0 to 100.

Ⓐ 45
Ⓑ 54
Ⓒ 77
Ⓓ 80
Ⓔ 95

5. Select all the numbers you would say if you were counting by 100's from 100 to 1,000.

Ⓐ 300
Ⓑ 330
Ⓒ 760
Ⓓ 755
Ⓔ 800

6. Start at 210 and count by 5's. What is the 6th number you say?

- Ⓐ 710
- Ⓑ 270
- Ⓒ 770
- Ⓓ 240

7. Identify the pattern of the numbers by placing a check-mark under the column.

	5s	10s	100s
310, 410, 510, 610, 710, 810			
305, 310, 315, 320, 325, 330			
715, 725, 735, 745, 755, 765			
400, 405, 410, 415, 420, 425			

8. Complete the table by filling in the missing numbers from each pattern.

	545	555		575
803				843
	325	425		
800			830	

9. Ted says that you can start at any number and count by 10s and every number in the pattern will end in a zero. Is Ted correct? Explain your answer.

10. Select the numbers you would say if you were counting by 5s from 230 to 250.

- Ⓐ 235
- Ⓑ 255
- Ⓒ 240
- Ⓓ 265

Chapter 2

Lesson 4: Read And Write Numbers To 1000 Using Base-ten Numerals

You can scan the QR code given below or use the url to access additional EdSearch resources including videos and mobile apps related to *Read And Write Numbers To 1000 Using Base-ten Numerals.*

 Search

Read And Write Numbers To 1000 Using Base-ten Numerals

URL	QR Code
http://www.lumoslearning.com/a/2nbta3	

1. **How is 458 written in expanded form?**

   Ⓐ 400 + 500 + 800
   Ⓑ 45 + 8
   Ⓒ 400 + 50 + 8
   Ⓓ 400 + 58

2. **Which number is five hundred thirty?**

   Ⓐ 503
   Ⓑ 530
   Ⓒ 533
   Ⓓ 513

3. **What is 200 + 8 written in standard form?**

   Ⓐ 280
   Ⓑ 288
   Ⓒ 208
   Ⓓ 2008

4. **What is 167 written in word form?**

   Ⓐ One hundred sixty-seven
   Ⓑ One hundred six hundred seven
   Ⓒ One hundred six seventy
   Ⓓ One hundred sixty

5. **Select the correct way to write 734 in word and expanded form.**

   Ⓐ 700 + 34
   Ⓑ Seven hundred thirty-four
   Ⓒ Seventy thirty-four
   Ⓓ 700 + 30 + 4
   Ⓔ 730 + 4

6. **Select the correct way to write 480 in word and expanded form.**

   Ⓐ Four hundred eight
   Ⓑ Four hundred eighty-eight
   Ⓒ Four hundred eighty
   Ⓓ 400+80+0
   Ⓔ 400+80

7. What number is expressed as 500 + 2 in expanded form?

8. Match the table with the correct number.

	437	430	473	407
Four hundred seven				
400 + 30				
Four hundred seventy-three				
400 +30 +7				

9. Complete the table by filling in the different forms under each column.

STANDARD	EXPANDED	WORD
444	400 + 40 + 4	
	300 + 8	Three hundred eight
		Nine hundred twenty five
	400 + 10	

10. Mya says 300 written in expanded form is 300. Trevor says that 300 written in expanded form is 300 + 0 + 0. Who is correct? Explain your reasoning.

Chapter 2

Lesson 5: Compare Two Three-digit Numbers

You can scan the QR code given below or use the url to access additional EdSearch resources including videos and mobile apps related to *Compare Two Three-digit Numbers*.

 **Search**   *Compare Two Three-digit Numbers*

URL	QR Code
http://www.lumoslearning.com/a/2nbta4	

1. Choose the symbol that goes in the blank in the number sentence.
    458 _____ 485

Ⓐ >
Ⓑ <
Ⓒ =

2. Choose the symbol that goes in the blank in the number sentence.
    276 _____ 267

Ⓐ >
Ⓑ <
Ⓒ =

3. Choose the symbol that goes in the blank in the number sentence.
    408 _____ 480

Ⓐ >
Ⓑ <
Ⓒ =

4. Choose the comparison that is correct.

Ⓐ 212 > 221
Ⓑ 986 < 968
Ⓒ 521 = 512
Ⓓ 761 > 716

5. Choose the comparison that is correct.

Ⓐ 400 + 50 + 2 < 400 + 20 + 5
Ⓑ 312 > 300 + 20 + 1
Ⓒ 400 + 60 + 2 = 462
Ⓓ 900 = 900 + 90

6. Select all of the comparisons that are correct.

Ⓐ 413 < 400 + 30 + 1
Ⓑ 500 + 60 + 8 = 568
Ⓒ 100 + 70 + 7 > 700 + 70 + 1
Ⓓ 200 + 2 < 200 + 20
Ⓔ 777 = 700 + 70

7. Which number is the greatest between 324, 342, 234, 243?

8. Place a check mark under the correct column to complete each comparison.

	>	<	=
459 ___ 495			
233 ___ 200 + 30 + 1			
700 + 70 ___ 700 + 7			
200 + 40 ___ 240			

9. Complete the table by filling in greater than, less than, or equal to.

458 is		485
302 is		300 + 2
798 is		700 + 80 + 9
390 is		300 + 9
900 + 70 + 5 is		957

10. Michael had 103 marbles in a jar. Julie had 100 marbles in a vase and 30 marbles in a jar. Who had the most marbles? Explain your answer.

Chapter 2

Lesson 6: Add And Subtract Within 100 Using Place Values

You can scan the QR code given below or use the url to access additional EdSearch resources including videos and mobile apps related to *Add And Subtract Within 100 Using Place Values.*

 **Add And Subtract Within 100 Using Place Values**

URL	QR Code
http://www.lumoslearning.com/a/2nbtb5	

1. ? + 12 = 44

    Ⓐ 56
    Ⓑ 32
    Ⓒ 23
    Ⓓ 65

2. ? – 15 = 62

    Ⓐ 43
    Ⓑ 47
    Ⓒ 57
    Ⓓ 77

3. 21 + ? = 55

    Ⓐ 31
    Ⓑ 34
    Ⓒ 76
    Ⓓ 66

4. Select the equation that does NOT equal 76.

    Ⓐ 99 – 23 = ?
    Ⓑ 40 + 36 = ?
    Ⓒ 2 + 74 = ?
    Ⓓ 100 – 25 = ?

5. Select all of the equations that equal 68.

    Ⓐ 78 – 10 = ?
    Ⓑ 34 + 34 = ?
    Ⓒ 100 – 28 = ?
    Ⓓ 22 + 46 = ?
    Ⓔ 58 + 20 = ?

6. Select all of the equations that equal 23.

    Ⓐ 53 – 33 = ?
    Ⓑ 19 + 5 = ?
    Ⓒ 65 – 42 = ?
    Ⓓ 3 + 20 = ?
    Ⓔ 11 + 23 = ?

7. What number does x represent in the equation?

   $54 + x = 75$

8. Match each equation with the number it equals by placing a checkmark under the correct column.

	27	18	32
23 + ? = 41			
62 - ? = 30			
48 - ? = 21			

9. Complete the table by filling in each row.

29	+		=	66
	-	18	=	70
47	+	34	=	

10. Altogether, Jane and Kim have 76 pencils. Kim have 43 pencils. How many pencils does Jane have?

Chapter 2

Lesson 7: Add Four Two-digit Numbers

You can scan the QR code given below or use the url to access additional EdSearch resources including videos and mobile apps related to *Add Four Two-digit Numbers*.

 **Add Four Two-digit Numbers**

URL	QR Code
http://www.lumoslearning.com/a/2nbtb6	

1. Choose the correct sum for the equation
    $10 + 45 + 10 + 20 = ?$

    Ⓐ 75
    Ⓑ 85
    Ⓒ 55
    Ⓓ 80

2. Choose the correct sum for the equation
    $15 + 15 + 20 + 30 = ?$

    Ⓐ 80
    Ⓑ 30
    Ⓒ 50
    Ⓓ 75

3. Drew added how many points he scored in all of the four basketball games that he played. He scored 12 points the first game, 10 points the second game, 16 points the third game, and 8 points the fourth game. How many points did Drew score in all four games?

    Ⓐ 26
    Ⓑ 12
    Ⓒ 22
    Ⓓ 46

4. What is the sum of 28, 31, 5, and 19?

    Ⓐ 84
    Ⓑ 48
    Ⓒ 83
    Ⓓ 78

5. Which equation with two addends will give you the same answer as the following equation with four addends?
    $42 + 11 + 14 + 9 = ?$

    Ⓐ $53 + 14 = ?$
    Ⓑ $23 + 11 = ?$
    Ⓒ $42 + 11 = ?$
    Ⓓ $53 + 23 = ?$

6. Which way is NOT another way you can add 21 + 24 + 55 + 2 = ?

  Ⓐ (21 + 24) + (55 + 2) = ?
  Ⓑ (21 + 2) + (55 + 24) = ?
  Ⓒ (2 + 24) + (55 + 21) = ?
  Ⓓ (21 + 55) + (21 + 2) = ?

7. What is the sum of 43 + 54 + 20 + 5?

8. Match each equation with its correct sum by placing a check mark under the correct column for each equation. Some columns might have more than one check, some columns might not have a check.

	110	121	111
28 + 17 + 44 + 22			
39 + 18 + 24 + 29			
6 + 68 + 12 + 25			

9. Complete the table by entering the sum of the equations.

30 + 12 + 8 + 17	
1 + 11 + 30 + 44	
19 + 22 + 34 + 7	

10. Trey said you can solve the equation 30 + 5 + 5 + 30, by adding 60 and 10. Julie says that you can solve it by adding 35 + 35. Who is correct? Explain.

Chapter 2

Lesson 8: Add And Subtract Within 1000

You can scan the QR code given below or use the url to access additional EdSearch resources including videos and mobile apps related to *Add And Subtract Within 1000*.

 **Add And Subtract Within 1000**

URL	QR Code
http://www.lumoslearning.com/a/2nbtb7	

1. Solve: 763 – 211 = ?

    Ⓐ 974
    Ⓑ 551
    Ⓒ 972
    Ⓓ 552

2. Solve: 287 + 109 = ?

    Ⓐ 396
    Ⓑ 386
    Ⓒ 392
    Ⓓ 178

3. What is the sum of 418 and 220?

    Ⓐ 198
    Ⓑ 218
    Ⓒ 638
    Ⓓ 538

4. What is the difference between 733 and 190?

    Ⓐ 543
    Ⓑ 923
    Ⓒ 663
    Ⓓ 823

5. What is the value of x in the equation 109 + x = 309?

    Ⓐ 481
    Ⓑ 200
    Ⓒ 208
    Ⓓ 408

6. What is the value of x in the equation 385 – x = 300.

    Ⓐ 685
    Ⓑ 680
    Ⓒ 0
    Ⓓ 85

7. What is the difference between 825 and 399?

| |
| |

8. Match each equation with its correct sum or difference by placing a check mark under the correct column for each equation. Some columns might have more than one check, some columns might not have a check.

	313	303	302	312
124 + 179				
572 - 259				
491 - 189				
209 + 103				

9. Complete the table by filling in the missing numbers under each column.

308	+	433	=	
512	-	299	=	
275	+		=	412

10. Mike wants to buy a new T.V. The T.V. costs 458 dollars. He needs 255 more dollars to buy the T.V. If Mike needs 255 more dollars, how many dollars must he already have? Explain your answer and draw a model to explain.

| |
| |
| |
| |
| |
| |

Chapter 2

Lesson 9: Mental Addition And Subtraction In Steps Of 10

You can scan the QR code given below or use the url to access additional EdSearch resources including videos and mobile apps related to *Mental Addition And Subtraction In Steps Of 10*.

 **Mental Addition And Subtraction In Steps Of 10**

URL	QR Code
http://www.lumoslearning.com/a/2nbtb8	

1. What number is 10 more than 458?

Ⓐ 558
Ⓑ 448
Ⓒ 468
Ⓓ 358

2. What is 100 less than 450?

Ⓐ 350
Ⓑ 550
Ⓒ 340
Ⓓ 540

3. 678 is 10 less than what number?

Ⓐ 778
Ⓑ 578
Ⓒ 668
Ⓓ 688

4. 743 is 100 more than what number?

Ⓐ 753
Ⓑ 843
Ⓒ 643
Ⓓ 733

5. Which statement is true?

Ⓐ 399 is 10 more than 299.
Ⓑ 418 is 10 less than 408.
Ⓒ 977 is 100 more than 877.
Ⓓ 208 is 10 more than 218.

6. Select all of the true statements below.

Ⓐ 877 is 10 less than 887.
Ⓑ 480 is 100 less than 380.
Ⓒ 763 is 10 more than 663.
Ⓓ 111 is 100 less than 211.
Ⓔ 689 is 10 more than 699.

7. What number is 10 more than 999?

8. Place a check mark under each column that make the statements true.

	10 more	10 less	100 more	100 less
546 is ___ than 536				
297 is ___ than 397				
891 is ___ than 901				
1000 is ___ than 900				

9. Complete the table by filling in the missing columns.

402	is 10 more than	
543		643
114	is 100 more than	
297	is 10 more than	

10. Julie bought three new books. Her 1st book had 307 pages. Her 2nd book had 10 less than pages. Her 3rd book had 100 more than the second book. How many pages did the 2nd and 3rd book have? Explain your answer.

Chapter 2

Lesson 10: Explain Why Addition And Subtraction Strategies Work

You can scan the QR code given below or use the url to access additional EdSearch resources including videos and mobile apps related to *Explain Why Addition And Subtraction Strategies Work.*

 **Explain Why Addition And Subtraction Strategies Work**

URL	QR Code
http://www.lumoslearning.com/a/2nbtb9	

1. **What is another way to add 43 + 16?**

   Ⓐ (40 + 10) + (3 + 6)
   Ⓑ (40 + 1) + (30 + 6)
   Ⓒ (34) + (61)
   Ⓓ (4 + 1) + (30 + 60)

2. **What is another way to add 27 + 12?**

   Ⓐ (20 + 70) + (1 + 2)
   Ⓑ (20 + 10) + (7 + 2)
   Ⓒ (71 + 22)
   Ⓓ (72 + 21)

3. **What is another way to add 31 + 67?**

   Ⓐ (60 + 30) + (1 + 7)
   Ⓑ (6 + 3) + (70 + 40)
   Ⓒ (30 + 6) + (40 + 7)
   Ⓓ (43 + 76)

4. **(40 + 10) + (6 + 5) could be another way to add which equation below?**

   Ⓐ 64 + 51 = ?
   Ⓑ 14 + 9 = ?
   Ⓒ 46 + 15 = ?
   Ⓓ 406 + 105 = ?

5. **What is another equation that can solve 400 – 145?**

   Ⓐ 400 + 145 = ?
   Ⓑ 400 – 10 – 40 – 5 = ?
   Ⓒ 400 – 100 – 40 – 5 = ?
   Ⓓ 400 – 14 - 5 = ?

6. **What is another way to subtract 560 – 238?**

   Ⓐ 500 – 60 – 200
   Ⓑ 560 – 200 – 30 – 8
   Ⓒ 560 – 23 – 8
   Ⓓ 560 – 20 – 30 – 8

7. Write another way to represent 468 – 200 – 50 – 4 = 214.

```
┌──────────────────────────────────────────────┐
│                                                │
│                                                │
│                                                │
└──────────────────────────────────────────────┘
```

8. Match each statement with the strategy that will work **BEST** to solve the equation.

	300 - 158 =	389 - 274 =	35 + 23 ≈
Take the digits in the tens place and add them together, then take the digit in the ones place and add them together. Then add the total from the tens and the ones to get the final answer.			
Take the digits in the subtrahend and subtract the value of each from the minuend.			
Subtract 1 from the minuend and 1 from the subtrahend. Now, subtract the minuend and subtrahend to get the difference.			

9. Complete each table by filling in the equations for each given strategy.

589 - 300 - 50 - 2 = 237	
599 - 117 = 482	
(300 + 400) + (30 + 20) + (8 + 1) = 759	

10. Bill said that adding 23 + 45 will get you the same answer as adding 25 + 43. Is Bill correct? Explain you answer.

```
┌──────────────────────────────────────────────┐
│                                                │
│                                                │
│                                                │
│                                                │
│                                                │
│                                                │
└──────────────────────────────────────────────┘
```

Chapter 2

Lesson 11: Bundle Of Tens

You can scan the QR code given below or use the url to access additional EdSearch resources including videos and mobile apps related to *Bundle Of Tens*.

Bundle Of Tens

URL	QR Code
http://www.lumoslearning.com/a/2nbtb9	

1. What number is represented below?

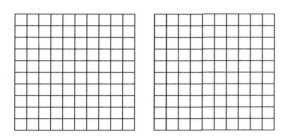 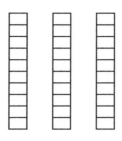

Ⓐ 213
Ⓑ 321
Ⓒ 231
Ⓓ 132

2. What number is 9 ones, 3 tens, 8 hundreds?

Ⓐ 938
Ⓑ 389
Ⓒ 839
Ⓓ 398

3. Which choice below is the same as 419?

Ⓐ 1 hundred, 4 tens, 9 ones
Ⓑ 9 ones, 4 hundreds, 1 ten
Ⓒ 4 ones, 1 ten, 9 hundreds
Ⓓ 1 hundred, 9 tens, 1 one

4. How many hundreds can be taken from 88 tens?

Ⓐ 80
Ⓑ 8
Ⓒ 88
Ⓓ 800

5. Which choice represents 213?

Ⓐ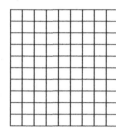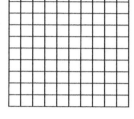

Ⓑ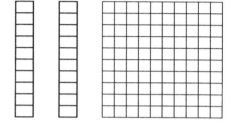

Ⓒ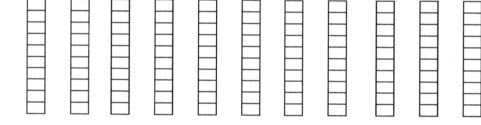

Ⓓ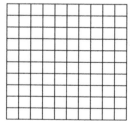

6. Choose the choice that the blocks below represent.

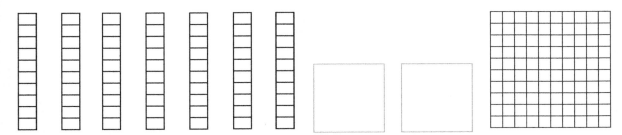

Ⓐ 7 hundreds, 1 ten, 2 ones
Ⓑ 7 tens , 2 hundreds, 1 one
Ⓒ 1 hundred, 2 ones, 7 tens
Ⓓ 2 hundreds, 7 tens, 2 ones

7. What number is represented by the blocks?

8. Place a check under the correct column to tell whether the number is less than 300 or more than 300.

	Less than 300	More than 300
13 tens, 200 ones		
14 tens, 150 ones		
27 tens, 3 ones		
15 ones, 20 tens		

9. Fill in the missing columns for each row to complete the table.

Ones	Tens	Hundreds	Number
7	4	3	
9	12		229
200	0		200

10. **Kayla said 345 can be unbundled into 3 hundreds and 45 ones. Is there another way to unbundled 345? Explain your answer.**

Chapter 2:
Number & Operations in Base Ten
Answer Key
&
Detailed Explanations

Lesson 1: Three Digit Numbers

Question No.	Answer	Detailed Explanations
1	C	The answer is C because there are 4 hundreds, 2 tens, and 3 ones.
2	B	The answer is B. There is one hundreds block and three tens block. 100 + 10 + 10 + 10 = 130.
3	A	The answer is A. 3 hundreds, 2 tens, and 7 ones is 327.
4	D	The answer is D. 5 hundreds, 6 tens, and 8 ones is 568.
5	B	The answer is B. 58 has 5 tens and 8 ones, but it does not have hundreds.
6	B	The answer is B. 340 does not have ones.
7	10	The answer is 10. It takes 10 tens to make one hundred. Students can use place value blocks, count by 10, repeated addition, etc to figure out the answer if they do not already know this concept.
8		8 ones, 3 tens, 5 hundreds --> 538 8 hundreds, 5 tens, 3 ones --> 853 8 tens, 3 ones, 5 hundreds --> 583 5 ones, 3 hundreds, 8 tens --> 385

Question 9

Ones	Hundreds	Tens	Number
8	4	5	**458**
7	0	**3**	37
4	**9**	**7**	974

Question 10

Sam's number is a three-digit number. There are 4 ones. There are 15 tens. 10 tens bundle together to make one hundred. Sam's number is 154. When I bundled 10 of the 15 tens, I had 5 tens left.

Sample Illustration Work

HUNDREDS	TENS	ONES
O	OOOOO OOOOO OOOOO	OOOO
1	5	4

Lesson 2: Count In Hundreds

Question No.	Answer	Detailed Explanations
1	A	The answer is A. There are 10 tens in a hundred. If there are 5 hundreds then it is 10 + 10 + 10 + 10 + 10 = 50.
2	B	The answer is B. Each block represents a hundred. There are 3 hundred blocks so there are 3 groups of 100.
3	C	The answer is C. There are 100 ones in a hundred. If there are 2 hundred blocks then 100 + 100 = 200 ones.
4	A	The answer is A. There are 4 hundreds blocks. So 400 is represented.
5	A	The answer is B. 80 tens equals 800. 800 equals 8 hundreds.
6	C	The answer is 3. 10 blocks equal a hundred. You can bundle 3 groups of ten from the blocks above.
7	7	The answer is 7. 6 hundred blocks represents 6 hundreds. 10 ten block represent 1 hundred. 6 hundreds + 1 hundred = 7 hundreds (700).
8		Blake is incorrect. 700 ones is equivalent to 70 tens. There are 10 ones in every ten. There are 100 ones in one hundred. So 700 ones is 7 hundreds. There are 10 tens in every hundred. 70 tens is 7 hundreds. That is why 700 ones is equivalent to 70 tens.
9		The problems can be solved by counting and bundling every ten base-ten blocks into one hundred.

10		IMAGE	Hundreds	Tens	Ones
		1	6	60	**600**
		2	**3**	30	300
		3	8	**80**	**800**
		4	**9**	**90**	**900**

Lesson 3: Count Within 1000

Question No.	Answer	Detailed Explanations
1	D	The answer is D. The pattern is counting by 5s and the next number is 255.
2	A	The answer is A. The pattern is counting by 100s, so the missing number is 300.
3	D	The answer is D. If you start at 67 and count by tens from 67 you say 77, 87, 97, 107. 107 is the 4th number.
4	A, D, & E	The answers are A, D, & E.
5	A & E	The answers are A & E.
6	D	The answer is D.
7		310, 410, 510, 610, 710, 810 --> 100s 305, 310, 315, 320, 325, 330 --> 5s 715, 725, 735, 745, 755, 765 --> 10s 400, 405, 410, 415, 420, 425 --> 5s

8

535	545	555	565	575
803	813	823	833	843
225	325	425	525	625
800	810	820	830	840

9		Ted is not correct. When you start at a number and count by 10s the number in the ones place does not change. If you start counting by 10s from the number 18, then every number in the pattern will end in 8.
10	A & C	Answer A and C is the correct answer.

Lesson 4: Read And Write Numbers To 1000 Using Base-ten Numerals

Question No.	Answer	Detailed Explanations
1	C	The answer is C. When writing a number in expanded form you add the value of each number. A 4 in the hundreds place has a value of 400. A 5 in the tens place has a value of 50. A 8 in the ones place has a value of 8.
2	B	The answer is B. 530.
3	C	The answer is C. When writing a number in expanded form you add the value of each number. A 2 in the hundreds place has a value of 200. A 8 in the ones place has a value of 8.
4	A	The answer is A. When writing a number, you write the number how you say it. It is important that students remember to not say "and" when saying whole numbers.
5	B & D	The answers are B & D. When writing a number in expanded form you add the value of each digit. When writing a number in word form, you write the number how you say it.
6	C & D	The answers are C & D. When writing a number in expanded form you add the value of each digit. When writing a number in word form, you write the number how you say it.
7	502	502
8		Four hundred seven --> 407 400 + 30 --> 430 Four hundred seventy-three --> 473 400 +30 +7 --> 437

Question 9

STANDARD	EXPANDED	WORD
444	400 + 40 + 4	**Four hundred forty four**
308	300 + 8	Three hundred eight
925	**900 + 20 + 5**	Nine hundred twenty five
410	400 + 10	**Four hundred ten**

| 10 | | Mya is correct. When writing a number in expanded form you add the values of each digit. You do not include 0 in expanded form. Even though Trevor's answer would still equal 300, that is not the correct way to write 300 in expanded form. |

Lesson 5: Compare Two Three-digit Numbers

Question No.	Answer	Detailed Explanations
1	B	The answer is B. When comparing numbers, you can begin in the highest places and compare the digits in that place. If the digits are the same, you can move to the next lower place. The 4s in the hundreds place are the same, so you move to the tens place. 8 is greater than 5, so 485 is greater than 458.
2	A	The answer is A. When comparing numbers, you can begin in the highest places and compare the digits in that place. If the digits are the same, you can move to the next lower place. The 2s in the hundreds place are the same, so you move to the tens place. 7 is greater than 6, so 276 is greater than 267.
3	B	The answer is B. When comparing numbers, you can begin in the highest places and compare the digits in that place. If the digits are the same, you can move to the next lower place. The 4s in the hundreds place are the same, so you move to the tens place. 8 is greater than 0, so 480 is greater than 408.
4	D	The answer is D. When comparing numbers, you can begin in the highest places and compare the digits in that place. If the digits are the same, you can move to the next lower place.
5	C	The answer is C. When numbers are in different forms, then you should convert each number to standard from before comparing. When comparing numbers, you can begin in the highest places and compare the digits in that place. If the digits are the same, you can move to the next lower place.
6	A, B & D	The answers are A, B, & D. When numbers are in different forms, then you should convert each number to standard from before comparing. When comparing numbers, you can begin in the highest places and compare the digits in that place. If the digits are the same, you can move to the next lower place.
7	342	342
8		$459 < 495$ $233 > 200 + 30 + 1$ $700 + 7 > 700 + 7$ $200 + 40 = 240$

Question No.	Answer	Detailed Explanations
9		458 is **less than** 485 302 is **equal to** 300 + 2 798 is **greater than** 700 + 80 + 9 390 is **greater than** 300 + 9 900 + 70 + 5 is **greater than** 957
10		Julie had the most marbles. If she had 100 marbles in a vase and 30 in a jar, she had a total of 130 marbles. 130 is greater than 103.

Lesson 6: Add And Subtract Within 100 Using Place Values

Question No.	Answer	Detailed Explanations
1	B	The answer is B. When finding a missing addend, you can subtract the other addend from the whole. 44 minus 12 equals 32.
2	D	The answer is D. To find a missing minuend in a subtraction problem, you add the subtrahend to the difference.
3	B	The answer is 34. When finding a missing addend, you can subtract the other addend from the whole. 55 minus 21 equals 34.
4	D	The answer is D. 100 minus 25 equals 75. It does NOT equal 76.
5	A, B & D	The answers are A, B, & D. 78 minus 10 equals 68. 34 plus 34 equals 68. 22 plus 46 equals 68.
6	C & D	The answers are C & D. 65 minus 42 equals 23. 3 plus 20 equals 23.
7	21	The answer is 21. The answer can be found by subtracting 75 minus 54 equals 21. So that means that 54 plus 21 equals 75. So x equals 21.
8		$23 + \mathbf{18} = 41$ $62 - \mathbf{32} = 30$ $48 - \mathbf{27} = 21$
9		<table><tr><td>29</td><td>+</td><td>37</td><td>=</td><td>66</td></tr><tr><td>88</td><td>-</td><td>18</td><td>=</td><td>70</td></tr><tr><td>47</td><td>+</td><td>34</td><td>=</td><td>81</td></tr></table>
10		Jane has 33 pencils. I know this because they have 76 pencils in all. If Kim have 43, then 76 minus 43 equals 33. So Jane has to have 33 pencils so that altogether they will have 76.

Name _____   Date _____

Lesson 7: Add Four Two-digit Numbers

Question No.	Answer	Detailed Explanations
1	B	The answer is B. You can set the problem up vertically to add them altogether, or you can break it apart and add two numbers at a time. 10 + 45 = 55/ 55 + 10 = 65 / 65 + 20 = 85.
2	A	The answer is A. You can set the problem up vertically to add them altogether, or you can break it apart and add two numbers at a time. 15 + 15 = 30/ 30 + 20 = 50 / 50 + 30 = 80.
3	D	The answer is 46. You can set the problem up vertically to add them altogether, or you can break it apart and add two numbers at a time. 12 + 10 = 22/ 22 + 16 = 38 / 38 + 8 = 46.
4	C	The answer is C. You can set the problem up vertically to add them altogether, or you can break it apart and add two numbers at a time.
5	D	The answer is D. You can take 42 + 11 (53) and 14 + 9 (23) and add them together to get the answer. 53 plus 23 equals 76.
6	D	The answer is D. 21 + 24 + 55 + 2 = 102. If you add 21 + 55, the answer is 76. If you add 21 + 2, the answer is 23. 76 plus 23 equals 99, so it is NOT another way to add the equation.
7	122	The answer is 122.
8		28 + 17 + 44 + 22 = **111** 39 + 18 + 24 + 29 = **110** 6 + 68 + 12 + 25 = **111**
9		30 + 12 + 8 + 17 = 67 1 + 11 + 30 + 44 = 86 19 + 22 + 34 + 7 = 82
10		They both are correct. Trey added the numbers that are the same first. 30 doubled is 60. 5 doubled is 10. So he added 60 + 10 = 70. Julie added the numbers together in order. 30 + 5 is 35 and 5 + 30 is 35. 35 + 35 = 70.

Lesson 8: Add And Subtract Within 1000

Question No.	Answer	Detailed Explanations
1	D	The answer is D. 763 minus 211 equals 552.
2	A	The answer is A. 287 plus 109 equals 396.
3	C	The answer is C. Sums are answers to addition problems. 418 plus 220 equals 638.
4	A	The answer is A. Differences are answers to subtraction problems. 733 minus 190 equals 543.
5	B	The answer is B. In order to find the missing part (addend), you can subtract the other addend from the whole sum. 309 − 109 = 200. So x has a value of 200 because 109 plus 200 equals 309.
6	D	The answer is D. To find the missing part, you can subtract the whole difference from the minuend. 385 minus 300 equals 85, so x has a value of 85. 385 minus 85 equals 300.
7	426	The answer is 426.
8		When we add 124 and 179 we get 303 572-259 gives 313 491-189 gives 302 and 209 +103 is 312
9		308 + 433 = **741** 512 - 299 = **213** 275 + **137** = 412
10		Mike already has 203 dollars. I know because the T.V. is the whole amount and costs 458 dollars. If he needs 255 more, I subtracted that from the whole. 203 dollars was the difference. So I know that he needs 203 dollars. I checked my answer using the equation 203 + 255 = 458.

Lesson 9: Mental Addition And Subtraction In Steps Of 10

Question No.	Answer	Detailed Explanations
1	C	The answer is C. When adding or subtracting 10, the only digit that changes is the digit in the tens place unless it is necessary to bundle.
2	A	The answer is A. When adding or subtracting 100,, the only digit that changes is the digit in the hundreds place unless it is necessary to bundle.
3	D	The answer is D. When adding or subtracting 10, the only digit that changes is the digit in the tens place.
4	C	The answer is C. When adding or subtracting 100,, the only digit that changes is the digit in the hundreds place unless it is necessary to bundle.
5	C	The answer is C. When adding or subtracting 100,, the only digit that changes is the digit in the hundreds place unless it is necessary to bundle.
6	A & D	The answers are A & D. When adding or subtracting 100, the only digit that changes is the digit in the hundreds place unless it is necessary to bundle.
7	1,009	The answer is 1,009. When adding or subtracting 100, the only digit that changes is the digit in the hundreds place unless it is necessary to bundle.
8		546 is **10 more** than 536 297 is **100 less** than 397 891 is **10 less** than 901 1000 is **100 more** than 900
9		402 is 10 more than **392** 543 **is 100 less than** 643 114 is 100 more than **14** 297 is 10 more than **287**
10		Julie had 307 page in her 1st book. 297 is 10 less than 307, so her 2nd book had 297 pages. 397 is 100 more than 297, so her 3rd book has 397 pages.

Lesson 10: Explain Why Addition And Subtraction Strategies Work

Question No.	Answer	Detailed Explanations
1	A	The answer is A. The 4 and the 1 are in the tens place, so they have a Value of 40 and 10 and they equal 50. The 3 and 6 are in the ones place And they have a value of 3 and 6 and they equal 9. 50 plus 9 equals 59.
2	B	The answer is B. The 2 and the 1 are in the tens place, so they have a value of 20 and 10 and they equal 30. The 7 and 2 are in the ones place and they have a value of 7 and 2 and they equal 9. 30 plus 9 equals 39.
3	A	The answer is A. The 3 and the 6 are in the tens place, so they have a value 60 and 30 and they equal 90. The 4 and the 7 are in the ones place and They have a value of 1 and 7 and they equal 8. 90 plus 8 equals 98.
4	C	The answer is C. The 4 and 1 are in the tens place and they have a value of 40 and 10 and they equal 50. The 6 and 5 are in the ones place and they have a value of 6 and 5 and they equal 11. 50 plus 11 equals 61.
5	C	The answer is C. $400 - 100 = 300$/ $300 - 40 = 260$ / $260 - 5 = 255$. When subtracting you can break the subtrahend apart and subtract the value of each digit.
6	B	The answer is B. When subtracting you can break the subtrahend apart and subtract the value of each digit.
7	214	The answer is $468 - 254 = 214$. The student should be able to know the different strategies or have an understanding of place value to correctly combine the subtrahend.
8		One strategy to add is to first add the values of each digit in the same place. You can $30 + 20$ (50) and $5 + 3$ (8) to get 58. One strategy to subtract is to subtract the value of each digit in the subtrahend from the minuend. $389 - 200$ is 189. $189 - 70$ is 119. $119 - 4 = 115$. One strategy to avoid regrouping across zeros is to take away 1 from the minuend (299). If you take away 1 from the minuend, you have to also take away 1 from the subtrahend (157). The new problem does not involve regrouping. It is $299 - 157 = 142$.

Question No.	Answer	Detailed Explanations
9		589 – 352 =237 600 – 118 =482 338 + 421 =759
10		Bill is correct. When you are adding you can take the value of each digit and add the places together. Switching the digits in the ones places will still get you the same answer. 20 + 40 = 60. 3 + 5 = 8 and 5 + 3 = 8. So you will get the same answer adding 23 + 45 and 25 + 43. They both equal 68.

Lesson 11: Bundle Of Tens

Question No.	Answer	Detailed Explanations
1	C	The answer is 231. There are 2 hundred blocks, 3 tens blocks, and 1 one block.
2	C	The answer is C. 8 hundreds, 3 tens, and 9 ones is 839.
3	B	The answer is B. The number 419 has 4 hundreds, 1 ten, and 9 ones.
4	B	The answer is B. You can bundle 10 tens 8 times (80 tens). 8 bundles of ten tens is 800. So you can get 8 hundreds from 88 tens.
5	D	The answer is D. 213 should have 2 hundred blocks, 1 ten block. And 3 ones.
6	C	The answer is C. There is 1 hundred block, 7 ten blocks, and 2 ones.
7	152	The answer is 152. There are 15 tens. 10 of them will be bundled together to make 1 hundred. There are 5 tens left. 5 tens is equivalent to 50. There are 2 ones. 1 hundred, 5 tens, 2 ones is 152.
8		The answers can be found by adding the tens and ones together. The student should remember that 10 tens equals one hundred and 100 ones equals one hundred.
9		The answers can be found by students remembering to bundle as necessary 10 ones is 1 ten. 100 ones is 1 hundred. 10 tens is 1 hundred.
10		Yes, 345 can be unbundled correctly into 3 hundreds, 4 tens, and 5 ones. You can take the 45 ones and bundle 40 of the ones into 4 tens. There will be 5 ones.

Chapter 3: Measurement & Data

Lesson 1: Measuring Length Of Objects

You can scan the QR code given below or use the url to access additional EdSearch resources including videos and mobile apps related to *Measuring Length Of Objects*.

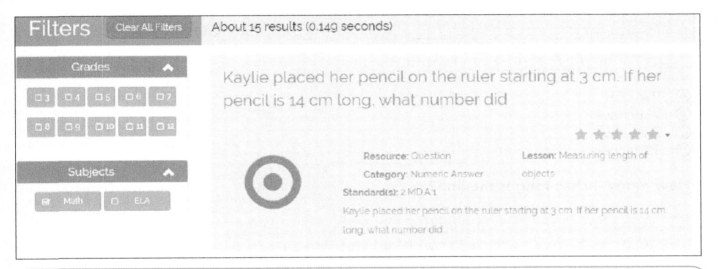

Filters   Clear All Filters   About 15 results (0.149 seconds)

Grades

☐3 ☐4 ☐5 ☐6 ☐7

☐8 ☐9 ☐10 ☐11 ☐12

Subjects

☑ Math   ☐ ELA

Kaylie placed her pencil on the ruler starting at 3 cm. If her pencil is 14 cm long, what number did

★ ★ ★ ★ ★

Resource: Question   Lesson: Measuring length of
Category: Numeric Answer   objects
Standard(s): 2.MD.A.1
Kaylie placed her pencil on the ruler starting at 3 cm. If her pencil is 14 cm long, what number did

---

ed Search   *Measuring Length Of Objects*

URL	QR Code
http://www.lumoslearning.com/a/2mda1	

1. How many inches long is the line below?

   Ⓐ   8 inches
   Ⓑ   18 inches
   Ⓒ   80 inches
   Ⓓ   1/8 inches

2. How many inches long is the line?

   Ⓐ   9 inches
   Ⓑ   2 inches
   Ⓒ   7 inches
   Ⓓ   12 inches

3. How many inches long is the line?

   Ⓐ   3 inches
   Ⓑ   12 inches
   Ⓒ   9 inches
   Ⓓ   36 inches

4. Brad cut a piece of string that is 4 inches. What choice below can represent Brad's string?

Ⓐ

Ⓑ

Ⓒ

Ⓓ

5. Lucy drew a line that was 7 inches. Select all of the possible representations of Lucy's line.

Ⓐ

Ⓑ

Ⓒ

Ⓓ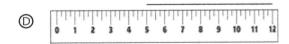

Ⓔ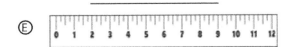

6. **Travis cut a piece of ribbon that was 9 cm long. Which one of the following choices could be where Travis placed the ribbon on the ruler?**

   Ⓐ Travis' ribbon began on 3 cm and ended on 9 cm
   Ⓑ Travis' ribbon began on 1 cm and ended on 9 cm
   Ⓒ Travis' ribbon ended on 14 cm and began on 5 cm
   Ⓓ Travis' ribbon ended on 19 cm and began on 27 cm

7. **Kaylie placed her pencil on the ruler starting at 3 cm. If her pencil is 14 cm long, what number did Kaylie's pencil end on?**

8. **Match each line on the ruler with its length in inches.**

	7 inches	2 inches	5 inches	9 inches
0 1 2 3 4 5 6 7 8 9 10 11 12				
0 1 2 3 4 5 6 7 8 9 10 11 12				
0 1 2 3 4 5 6 7 8 9 10 11 12				
0 1 2 3 4 5 6 7 8 9 10 11 12				

9. **Complete the table by using the points to draw lines on the ruler for the given length.**

8 inches	0 1 2 3 4 5 6 7 8 9 10 11 12
9 inches	0 1 2 3 4 5 6 7 8 9 10 11 12
10 inches	0 1 2 3 4 5 6 7 8 9 10 11 12

10. A line on a ruler starts at 1 and ends at 8. Pedro says the line is 8 inches because when you count to 8 you start at 1. Marie disagrees and says that the line is 7 inches. Who is correct? Explain your answer.

Chapter 3

Lesson 2: Measure Length Of Object Using Two Different Length Units

You can scan the QR code given below or use the url to access additional EdSearch resources including videos and mobile apps related to *Measure Length Of Object Using Two Different Length Units.*

 **Measure Length Of Object Using Two Different Length Units**

URL	QR Code
http://www.lumoslearning.com/a/2mda2	

1. Look at the ruler below, then choose the true statement.

- Ⓐ 2 inches is equivalent to 2 centimeters.
- Ⓑ Inches are shorter than centimeters.
- Ⓒ 7 centimeters is less than 3 inches.
- Ⓓ 12 centimeters is closer to 6 inches than 5 inches.

2. Look at the ruler below, then choose the true statement.

- Ⓐ 3 inches is between 7 and 8 centimeters.
- Ⓑ There are 12 centimeters in 4 inches.
- Ⓒ 8 centimeters is less than 3 inches.
- Ⓓ 5 inches is longer than 13 centimeters.

3. Look at the ruler below, then choose the statement that is NOT true.

- Ⓐ 1 inch is between 2 and 3 centimeters.
- Ⓑ 7 centimeters is less than 3 inches.
- Ⓒ 10 centimeters are less than 4 inches.
- Ⓓ 2 ½ inches is more than 7 centimeters.

4. Look at the ruler below, then choose the statement that is NOT true.

- Ⓐ 1 centimeter is less than ½ an inch.
- Ⓑ 7 centimeters is closer to 2 inches than 3 inches.
- Ⓒ 5 inches is less than 13 centimeters.
- Ⓓ 2 inches is closer to 5 centimeters than 6 centimeters.

5. **Look at the line on the ruler below. Choose the statement that correctly describes the measurement.**

Ⓐ The line is 8 inches long.
Ⓑ The line is 8 centimeters long.
Ⓒ The line is 3 inches long.
Ⓓ The line is 3 ½ inches long.

6. **Look at the line on the ruler below. Choose the true statement.**

Ⓐ The line is about 3 inches.
Ⓑ The line is about 3 centimeters.
Ⓒ The line is close to 8 inches.
Ⓓ The line is shorter than 4 centimeters.

7. **Kylie had a pencil that was 10 centimeters. She sharpened it and now it is 8 centimeters. How many centimeters were taken off when Kylie sharpened her pencil?**

8. **Look at the ruler below. Then match each statement as true or false by placing a check-mark under each column.**

	True	False
9 centimeters is shorter than $^3/_{12}$ inches		
4 ½ inches is between 11 and 12 centimeters		
5 inches is closer to 13 centimeters than 12 centimeters		

9. Complete the table by filling in the correct measurement of the line.

		centimeters
		inches
		centimeters
		inches

10. Amy said that if a ruler has at least 5 inches, then it will have at least 12 centimeters. Do you agree with Amy? Explain.

Chapter 3

Lesson 3: Estimate Lengths Using Different Units Of Measurement

You can scan the QR code given below or use the url to access additional EdSearch resources including videos and mobile apps related to *Estimate Lengths Using Different Units Of Measurement.*

Estimate Lengths Using Different Units Of Measurement

URL	QR Code
http://www.lumoslearning.com/a/2mda3	

1. The height of an orange is about 8 ___?

Ⓐ Centimeters
Ⓑ Feet
Ⓒ Inches
Ⓓ Meters

2. The length of a fork is about 6 _____ ?

Ⓐ Centimeters
Ⓑ Feet
Ⓒ Inches
Ⓓ Meters

3. The height of a door is about 7 ____?

Ⓐ Centimeters
Ⓑ Feet
Ⓒ Inches
Ⓓ Meters

4. The length of a paper clip is about 12 ___?

Ⓐ Centimeters
Ⓑ Feet
Ⓒ Inches
Ⓓ Meters

5. The length of a sheet of paper is about 18 _____?

Ⓐ Centimeters
Ⓑ Feet
Ⓒ Inches
Ⓓ Meters

6. The height of a refrigerator is about 2 ___?

Ⓐ Centimeters
Ⓑ Feet
Ⓒ Inches
Ⓓ Meters

7. Angelica <u>correctly</u> answered the question "About how many inches is a ruler?" What number did Angelica say?

8. Complete the table by filling in the unit that is the best estimate for each row.

	Centimeter	Feet	Inches	Meters
The height of a birthday candle is about 2 __?				
The height of a chair is about 1 __?				
The height of a box of cereal is about 12 __?				
The height of a vacuum cleaner is about 4 __?				

9. Complete the table by writing in the unit that is the best estimate for each row.

The height of a countertop is about 3 __?	
The length of a bottle of water is about 8 __	
The length of a football field is about 110 __	
The length of an ant is about 2 __	

10. Mya says that the height of the couch at her house is about 2 ½ inches. Did Mya say the correct unit? Explain how you know.

Chapter 3

Lesson 4: Compare The Length Of Objects

You can scan the QR code given below or use the url to access additional EdSearch resources including videos and mobile apps related to *Compare The Length Of Objects*.

Compare The Length Of Objects

URL	QR Code
http://www.lumoslearning.com/a/2mda4	

1. How much longer is Rectangle A than Rectangle B?

Rectangle A

Rectangle B

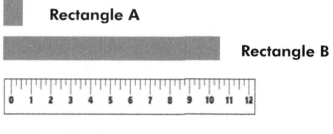

Ⓐ 3 ½ inches
Ⓑ 4 centimeters
Ⓒ 4 inches
Ⓓ 3 ½ centimeters

2. How much shorter is Rectangle A than Rectangle B?

Rectangle A

Rectangle B

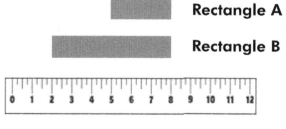

Ⓐ 10 ½ centimeters
Ⓑ 10 centimeters
Ⓒ 10 inches
Ⓓ 10 ½ inches

3. How much longer is Rectangle B than Rectangle A?

Rectangle A

Rectangle B

Ⓐ The rectangles are the same length.
Ⓑ 3 inches
Ⓒ 5 inches
Ⓓ 2 inches

4. How much longer is Rectangle A than Rectangle B?

Rectangle A

Rectangle B

Ⓐ 5 centimeters
Ⓑ 4 centimeters
Ⓒ 3 inches
Ⓓ 12 inches

5. Choose the correct comparison about Rectangle A and B below.

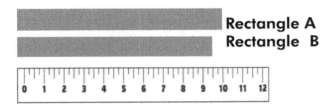

Rectangle A
Rectangle B

Ⓐ Rectangle A is 1 inch longer than Rectangle B.
Ⓑ Rectangle A is ½ centimeter longer than Rectangle B.
Ⓒ Rectangle B is ½ inch shorter than Rectangle A.
Ⓓ Rectangle B is 1 inch shorter than Rectangle B.

6. Choose the correct comparison about Rectangle A and B below.

Rectangle A

Rectangle B

Ⓐ Rectangle B is 4 inches longer than Rectangle A.
Ⓑ Rectangle A is 4 cm shorter than Rectangle B.
Ⓒ Rectangle A is 8 cm shorter than Rectangle B.
Ⓓ Rectangle B is 12 inches longer than Rectangle A.

LumosLearning.com

7. How many inches longer is Rectangle A than Rectangle B.

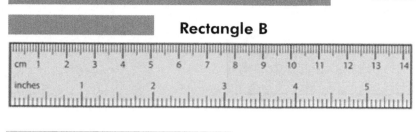

Rectangle A

Rectangle B

8. Bubble in the circle under the correct statement for each row.

	Line A is 6 cm shorter than Line B.	Line A and Line B are the same length.	Line A is 1 inch longer than Line B.	Line B is 4 inches shorter than Line A.
Line A / Line B	○	○	○	○
Line A / Line B	○	○	○	○
Line A / Line B	○	○	○	○
Line A / Line B	○	○	○	○

9. Fill in the correct number of line on the blank in the table to show the difference between the rectangles below.

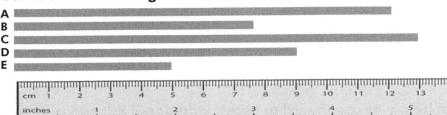

Line A is		Then Line D.
Line B is	2 inches shorter than	
	7 cm shorter	Then Line A.
All lines are	Longer than 3 inches except	
All lines are	Shorter than 12 cm except	

10. Miley said that 5 cm is longer than 3 inches because 5 is the greater number. Is Miley correct? Explain your answer.

Chapter 3

Lesson 5: Addition And Subtraction Word Problems Within 100

You can scan the QR code given below or use the url to access additional EdSearch resources including videos and mobile apps related to *Addition And Subtraction Word Problems Within 100*.

 **Addition And Subtraction Word Problems Within 100**

URL	QR Code
http://www.lumoslearning.com/a/2mdb5	

1. Brian had a piece of string that measures 36 inches. He cut the string and now the string is 12 inches. How much string did Brian cut?

   Ⓐ 12 inches
   Ⓑ 36 inches
   Ⓒ 24 inches
   Ⓓ 48 inches

2. The hallway from the cafeteria door to the office door is about 65 feet. From the office door to the gym door is about 30 feet. About how many feet is it from the cafeteria door to the gym door?

   Ⓐ About 95 feet
   Ⓑ About 30 feet
   Ⓒ About 35 feet
   Ⓓ About 65 feet

3. Lola cut 3 pieces of string all the same length in inches. The total length of all 3 pieces of string is 12 inches combined. What is the length of each piece of string?

   Ⓐ 12 inches
   Ⓑ 6 inches
   Ⓒ 3 inches
   Ⓓ 4 inches

4. Trevor's ink pen is 4 inches long. If he has 5 ink pens, what is the total length of all the pens if they were lined up?

   Ⓐ 9 inches
   Ⓑ 16 inches
   Ⓒ 20 inches
   Ⓓ 25 inches

5. Kim's jump rope is 94 inches. Her little sister's jump rope is 60 inches. How much longer is Kim's jump rope than her little sister's jump rope?

   Ⓐ 30 inches
   Ⓑ 34 inches
   Ⓒ 102 inches
   Ⓓ 88 inches

6. Mark has two dogs, Pebbles and Bits. Pebbles is 27 inches tall. Bits is 11 inches tall. How much shorter is Bits than Pebbles?

    Ⓐ 16 inches
    Ⓑ 38 inches
    Ⓒ 37 inches
    Ⓓ 17 inches

7. Taylor is 57 inches tall. Jacob is 9 inches shorter than Taylor. How many inches tall is Jacob?

8. Choose the correct answer for each row by bubbling in the circle for the correct column.

	True	False
Jessica walked 78 feet. Lucy walked 99 feet. Lucy walked 11 feet more than Jessica.		
Peter had 53 cm of yarn. He used 21 cm. Peter now has 74 cm of yarn.		
Cooper is 15 inches shorter than Bryce. If Cooper is 50 inches, then Bryce is 65 inches.		

9. Complete the table by filling in the correct answer for each row.

Julie got a new hair cut. Julie's hair was 21 inches long. She cut off 13 inches. How many inches long is Julie's hair now?	
David's new bookcase is 96 inches tall. David is 75 inches tall. How much taller is David's bookcase than he is?	
Jordan is walking across the football field. He has walked 66 meters and he has 34 meters to go. How many meters long is the football field.	

10. Jasmine needs 67 feet of thread for her knitting project. She has 5 spools of thread and each spool has 10 feet of thread. How many more spools does Jasmine need to buy. Explain your answer.

Chapter 3

Lesson 6: Represent Whole Numbers As Lengths On A Number Line

You can scan the QR code given below or use the url to access additional EdSearch resources including videos and mobile apps related to *Represent Whole Numbers As Lengths On A Number Line*.

 **Represent Whole Numbers As Lengths On A Number Line**

URL	QR Code
http://www.lumoslearning.com/a/2mdb6	

1. 54 + ___ = 74

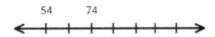

Ⓐ 10
Ⓑ 4
Ⓒ 64
Ⓓ 20

2. If you start at 15 and jump three times, what number will you land on?

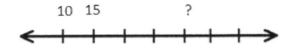

Ⓐ 30
Ⓑ 25
Ⓒ 15
Ⓓ 5

3. How many times will you jump to show 22 + 6?

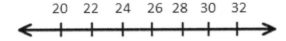

Ⓐ 2
Ⓑ 3
Ⓒ 6
Ⓓ 8

4. How many times will you jump to get from 35 to 45?

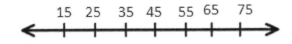

Ⓐ 1
Ⓑ 10
Ⓒ 2
Ⓓ 5

5. What number is 5 jumps from 12?

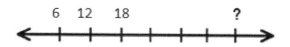

    Ⓐ 48
    Ⓑ 42
    Ⓒ 30
    Ⓓ 36

6. What number is 3 jumps from 21?

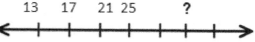

    Ⓐ 29
    Ⓑ 33
    Ⓒ 30
    Ⓓ 34

7. If each jump on the number line is 7, what number would replace the question mark?

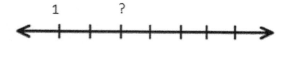

┌────────────────────────────────────┐
│   │
│   │
└────────────────────────────────────┘

8. Match each number line with the correct number to replace the question mark. All answers will not be used.

		20	18	22
8 13 ? 28				
6 14 18 ?				

9. Fill in the table with the correct number to replace the question mark on the number line.

3 13 **?** 43	
? 67 69 73	

10. Marco drew a number line with 7 increments of 10, starting with the number 10. Draw Marco's number line and place the correct number on the 4th line. Explain your answer.

Chapter 3

Lesson 7: Tell And Write Time From Clocks

You can scan the QR code given below or use the url to access additional EdSearch resources including videos and mobile apps related to *Tell And Write Time From Clocks*.

 **Tell And Write Time From Clocks**

URL	QR Code
http://www.lumoslearning.com/a/2mdc7	

1. Which time is shown on the clock below?

Ⓐ   5:05
Ⓑ   6:01
Ⓒ   1:06
Ⓓ   6:05

2. Which time is shown on the clock below?

Ⓐ   11:15
Ⓑ   3:55
Ⓒ   11:03
Ⓓ   11:20

3. Which time is shown on the clock below?

Ⓐ   9:30
Ⓑ   8:06
Ⓒ   8:30
Ⓓ   8:15

4. Mark has basketball practice at the time that is shown on the clock. What time does Mark have basketball practice.

Ⓐ 4:45
Ⓑ 4:00
Ⓒ 3:45
Ⓓ 3:09

5. The clock below shows the time. What time will it be in 5 minutes?

Ⓐ 12:03
Ⓑ 12:15
Ⓒ 12:20
Ⓓ 3:12

6. The below shows the time. 15 minutes ago, Byron got home. What time did Byron get home?

Ⓐ 1:00
Ⓑ 12:45
Ⓒ 1:45
Ⓓ 12:30

7. What time is shown on the clock below?

[blank answer box]

8. Match each clock with the column of its correct time. All columns will not be selected.

	4:15	2:45	1:45	7:30	6:30

9. Complete the table by writing the correct time shown on the clock.

(clock)	
(clock)	
(clock)	

10. Paul looked at the clock below and said that in 5 minutes it will be 11:45. Kesha says that in 5 minutes it will be 11:25. Who is correct? Explain.

Chapter 3

Lesson 8: Solve Word Problems Involving Money

You can scan the QR code given below or use the url to access additional EdSearch resources including videos and mobile apps related to *Solve Word Problems Involving Money*.

 **Solve Word Problems Involving Money**

URL	QR Code
http://www.lumoslearning.com/a/2mdc8	

1. How much money in all is 1 dollar, 3 dimes, and 4 pennies?

    Ⓐ $1.19
    Ⓑ $1.79
    Ⓒ $1.30
    Ⓓ $1.34

2. What is the value of 2 quarters, 3 dimes, 4 nickels, and 1 penny?

    Ⓐ $1.01
    Ⓑ $2.01
    Ⓒ $0.91
    Ⓓ $1.41

3. What is the value of 3 dollars, 4 quarters, and 6 pennies?

    Ⓐ $4.46
    Ⓑ $3.46
    Ⓒ $4.06
    Ⓓ $3.64

4. Billy has 6 quarters, 3 dimes, and 2 nickels. How much money does Billy have in all?

    Ⓐ $1.80
    Ⓑ $1.90
    Ⓒ $2.80
    Ⓓ $2.90

5. Corey has $0.76. Which group of coins can Corey possibly have?

    Ⓐ Two quarters, six pennies
    Ⓑ Three quarters, one dime
    Ⓒ Five dimes, one quarter, one penny
    Ⓓ Seven dimes, six quarters

6. Breya has $2.13. Which group of coins can Breya possibly have?

    Ⓐ One dollar bill, four quarters, two nickels, three pennies
    Ⓑ Two dollar bills, one dime, thirteen pennies
    Ⓒ One dollar bill, four quarters, three pennies
    Ⓓ Two dollar bills, one nickel, three pennies

7. What is the value of 7 quarters, 5 nickels, and 25 pennies?

```
┌─────────────────────────────┐
│                             │
│                             │
└─────────────────────────────┘
```

8. Match each combination of coins with the column of its correct total amount. All columns will not be selected.

	$1.47	$0.65	$1.57	$1.21	$1.65
4 quarters, 1 penny, 2 dimes					
2 dimes, 1 quarter, 10 pennies, 2 nickels					
9 dimes, 2 pennies, 1 nickel, 2 quarters					

9. Complete the table by filling in the value of the coins.

2 dollars, 1 quarter, 6 nickels, 1 dime	
5 dimes, 2 quarters, 3 nickels, 7 pennies	
3 quarters, 1 dollar, 3 dimes, 2 nickels, 20 pennies	

10. Bruce wants to buy a candy bar for $1.59. Bruce has 3 dimes, 3 quarters, and 11 nickels. Does he have enough money to buy the candy bar? Explain.

Chapter 3

Lesson 9: Generate Measurement Data

You can scan the QR code given below or use the url to access additional EdSearch resources including videos and mobile apps related to *Generate Measurement Data*.

 **Generate Measurement Data**

URL	QR Code
http://www.lumoslearning.com/a/2mdd9	

The measurement of Kim's pieces of ribbon are plotted on the line plot. Use the line plot below to answer all the questions.

Note: Each x represents 2 pieces of ribbon

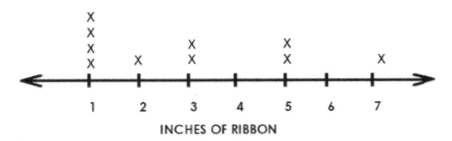

INCHES OF RIBBON

1. What lengths does none of Kim's ribbons measure?

Ⓐ 1 inch and 2 inches
Ⓑ 4 inches and 5 inches
Ⓒ 4 inches and 6 inches
Ⓓ 2 inches and 7 inches

2. How many pieces of ribbon does Kim have that is 7 inches?

Ⓐ 2
Ⓑ 1
Ⓒ 3
Ⓓ 0

3. How many pieces of Kim's ribbon is only 1 inch long?

Ⓐ 4
Ⓑ 2
Ⓒ 8
Ⓓ 6

4. Kim can only use the ribbon that is 3 or more inches. How many pieces of ribbon can Kim use?

Ⓐ 5
Ⓑ 10
Ⓒ 4
Ⓓ 12

5. IF there were three additional Xs plotted for the number 5, how many 5 inch pieces of ribbon WOULD Kim have?

  Ⓐ 4
  Ⓑ 2
  Ⓒ 5
  Ⓓ 10

6. Kim will throw away all pieces of ribbon that are under 3 inches. How many pieces of ribbon will Kim throw away?

  Ⓐ 10
  Ⓑ 5
  Ⓒ 4
  Ⓓ 1

7. How many pieces of ribbon does Kim have in all?

8. Use the line plot provided at the beginning of the lesson and select true or false for each statement.

	True	False
Kim has 4 more 1 inch ribbons than she have 3 inch ribbon.		
Kim has 1 piece of ribbon that is 2 inches.		
Kim has the same amount of 3 inch ribbon and 5 inch ribbon.		

9. Use the line plot provided at the beginning of the lesson and complete the table by filling in the correct sum.

If there were 3 Xs plotted on the 4, how many pieces of ribbon would Kim have that was 4 inches long?	
If Kim uses all of her 3 inch ribbons and 1 of her 5 inch ribbons, how many pieces of ribbon did Kim use?	

10. Kim needs 12 pieces of 1 inch ribbon to glue as decoration on her craft. If Kim cut all of 2-inch ribbon in half, will she have enough 1-inch pieces? Explain.

Note: Use the line plot provided at the beginning of the lesson.

Chapter 3

Lesson 10: Draw Graphs To Represent Data

You can scan the QR code given below or use the url to access additional EdSearch resources including videos and mobile apps related to *Draw Graphs To Represent Data.*

 **Draw Graphs To Represent Data**

URL	QR Code
http://www.lumoslearning.com/a/2mdd10	

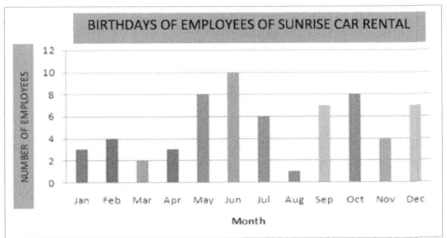

Use the bar graph to answer all the questions.

1. Which month had the fewest number of employee birthdays?

Ⓐ August
Ⓑ June
Ⓒ March
Ⓓ January

2. How many employees have a birthday in January?

Ⓐ 2
Ⓑ 4
Ⓒ 2 ½
Ⓓ 3

3. Which month had the most employee birthdays?

Ⓐ May
Ⓑ June
Ⓒ August
Ⓓ March

4. If Sunrise Car Rental gets a new employee that has a birthday in December, how many employees will have December birthdays?

Ⓐ 7
Ⓑ 8
Ⓒ 9
Ⓓ 6

5. How many more people have a birthday in March than in August?

    Ⓐ 2
    Ⓑ 1
    Ⓒ 3
    Ⓓ 0

6. The company is having a party to celebrate January & February birthdays together. How many people will they celebrate at the party?

    Ⓐ 3
    Ⓑ 4
    Ⓒ 6
    Ⓓ 7

7. All of Sunrise Car Rental's employees are included on the graph. How many employees do Sunrise Car Rental have?

8. Select true or false for each statement about the bar graph provided in the beginning of the lesson.

	True	False
The months with the most birthdays are May, June, and July.		
There are 6 more people with a birthday in September than in August.		
The same number of employees have birthdays in May and October.		

9. Use the bar graph provided in the beginning of the lesson and complete the table by filling in the correct month.

Which month has 4 fewer birthdays than June?	
Which month has the same number of birthdays as April?	
Which TWO months have four birthdays?	

10. Use the bar graph provided in the beginning of the lesson.

Cupcakes were ordered for everyone that has a birthday in May, June, and July. How many cupcakes were ordered in all?

Chapter 3:
Measurement & Data

Answer Key
&
Detailed Explanations

Name _____   Date _____

Lesson 1: Measuring Length Of Objects

Question No.	Answer	Detailed Explanations
1	A	The answer is A. The line starts at the beginning and ends on 8. The line Measures 8 inches.
2	C	The answer is 7 inches. The line starts on 2 and ends on 9. The difference between 9 and 2 is 7.
3	C	The answer is C. The line starts on 3 and ends on 12. The difference between 12 and 3 is 9.
4	B	The answer is B. The line starts on 7 and ends at 11. The difference between 11 and 7 is 4.
5	A, B, D, & E	The answers are A, B, D, & E. They all represent 7 inches. The difference of 7-0 is 7. The difference of $10 - 3 = 7$. The difference between $12 - 5 = 7$. The difference between $9 - 2 = 7$.
6	C	The answer is C because the difference between 14 and 5 is 9.
7	17 cm	The answer is 17cm. You should add how long it is to the place that Kaylie started on.
8		The difference between 11 and 2 is 9. The difference between 11 ½ and 4 ½ is 7. The difference between 11 and 9 is 2. The difference 7 and 2 is 5.
9		The first ruler should end on 9 because the difference between 9 and 1 (where the point is) is 8. The second ruler should begin on 2 because the difference between 11 and 2 is 9. You should move backwards on this problem, because the ruler isn't long enough to move forward. . The 3 rd ruler should start on 0 because the difference between 10 and 0 is 10. You should move backwards on this problem, because the ruler isn't long enough to move forward.
10		Marie is correct. A line should start on 0 to measure the same length as the number it starts on. If a line starts on 0 and ends at 8 it is 8 inches. If a line starts on 1 and ends on 8, it is 7 inches.

Lesson 2: Measure Length Of Object Using Two Different Length Units

Question No.	Answer	Detailed Explanations
1	C	The answer is C. If you look at the ruler, 7 centimeters come before 3 inches.
2	A	The answer is A. If you look at the ruler, 3 inches fall in between 7 and 8 centimeters.
3	D	The answer is D. If you look at the ruler, 2 ½ inches comes before 7 centimeters, which means it is less.
4	B	The answer is B. If you look at the ruler, 7 centimeters is closer to 3 inches than it is to 2 inches.
5	B	The answer is B. If you look at the ruler, the centimeters are at the top. The line begins at 0 centimeters and ends at 8 centimeters.
6	A	The correct answer is A. If you look at the ruler, the line is very close to 3 Inches. The inches are on the bottom of the ruler.
7	2 cm	The answer is 2 centimeters. The pencil was 10 and if it is now 8, the difference between 10 – 8 is 2.
8		9 centimeters is shorter than 3/12 inches --> False 4 1/2 inches is between 11 and 12 centimeters--> True 5 inches is closer to 13 centimeters than 12 centimeters--> True
9		6 centimeters 4 inches 8 centimeters 2 ½ inches
10		I agree with Amy because there are over 12 centimeters in 5 inches. If a ruler displays 5 inches, then 12 centimeters are in those 5 inches.

Lesson 3: Estimate Lengths Using Different Units Of Measurement

Question No.	Answer	Detailed Explanations
1	A	The answer is A. If you measure the height of an orange it should be CLOSER to 8 centimeters than any other unit. This is an estimate.
2	C	The answer is C. If you measure a fork it should be CLOSER to 6 inches than any other unit. This is an estimate.
3	B	The answer is B. If you measure a door it should be CLOSER to 7 feet than any other unit. This is an estimate.
4	A	The answer is A. If you measure a paperclip it should be CLOSER to 12 centimeters than any other unit. This is an estimate.
5	A	The answer is A. If you measure a sheet of paper it should be CLOSER to 18 centimeters than any other unit. This is an estimate.
6	D	The answer is D. If you measure the height of a refrigerator it should be CLOSER to 2 meters than any other unit. This is an estimate.
7	12	12 inches
8		The height of a birthday candle is about 2 **Centimeters** The height of a chair is about 1 **Meter** The height of a box of cereal is about 12 **Inches** The height of a vacuum cleaner is about 4 **Feet**
9		The height of a countertop is about 3 **Feet** The length of a bottle of water is about 8 **Inches** The length of a football field is about 110 **Meters** The length of an ant is about 2 **Centimeters**
10		Mya did not say the correct unit because 2 ½ inches is a very small couch that people could not sit on. Mya might have meant to say that it is 2 ½ feet.

Lesson 4: Compare The Length Of Objects

Question No.	Answer	Detailed Explanations
1	D	The answer is D. Rectangle B is 8 cm. Rectangle A is 11 ½ cm. The difference between 11 ½ and 8 is 3 ½.
2	C	The answer is C. Rectangle A is ½ inches. Rectangle B is 10 ½ inches. The difference between 10 ½ and ½ is 10.
3	B	The answer is B. Rectangle B starts on 2 inches and ends on 8 inches, so it is 6 inches in length. Rectangle A starts on 5 inches and ends on 8 inches, so it is 3 inches in length. The difference between 6 and 3 is 3.
4	A	The answer is A. Rectangle A starts on 2 cm and ends on 12 cm, so it is 10 cm in length. Rectangle B starts on 3 cm and ends on 8 cm, so it is 5 cm in length. The difference between 10 cm and 5 cm is 5 cm.
5	C	The answer is C. Rectangle B is 9 ½ inches and Rectangle A is 10 inches. The difference between 10 and 9 ½ is ½ .
6	B	The answer is B. Rectangle A is 8 cm. Rectangle B is 12 cm. The difference between 12 and 8 is 4 cm.
7	2 ½ inches	Rectangle B is 2 inches. Rectangle A 4 ½ inches. The difference between 4 ½ and 2 is 2 ½ .
8		Row 1: Line A is 1 inch longer than Line B Row 2: Line A is 6 cm shorter than Line B Row 3: Line B is 4 inches shorter than Line A Row 4: Line A and B are the same length
9		*(see table below)*
10		Miley is not correct. Even though 5 is greater than 3, inches are longer than cm. There is about 2 ½ cm in 1 inch. So 3 inches would be around 7 ½ inches.

Question 9:

Line A is	**3 cm longer**	Then Line D
Line B is	2 inches shorter than	**Line C**
Line E is	7 cm shorter	Then Line A
All lines are	Longer than 3 inches except	**Line E**
All lines are	Shorter than 12 cm except	**Line A & C**

Lesson 5: Addition And Subtraction Word Problems Within 100

Question No.	Answer	Detailed Explanations
1	C	The answer is C. You will need to subtract to get the answer. If Brian's string was 36 inches, but now is 12 inches, then he cut off 24 inches because the difference between 36 and 12 is 24.
2	A	The answer is A. You need to add to get the answer. If the cafeteria door is 65 feet from the office door and the office door is 30 from the gym, you need to add those two numbers to get the total feet all the way from the cafeteria, past the office, and to the gym.
3	D	The answer is D. If Lola's 3 pieces of string totals 12 inches and they are the same length then you should add the same number 3 times and get 12. 4 + 4 + 4 equals 12.
4	C	The answer is C. If each ink pen is 4 inches long and there are 5 ink pens, then 4 + 4 + 4 + 4 + 4 = 20.
5	B	The answer is B. You will need to subtract 94 − 60 to find the difference between the jump ropes. The difference between 94 minus 60 is 34.
6	A	The answer is A. You need to subtract to find the difference between Pebbles' height and Bits' height. 27 − 11 equals 16.
7	48 inches	The answer is 48 inches.
8		Jessica walked 78 feet. Lucy walked 99 feet. Lucy walked 11 feet more than Jessica. --> **False** Peter had 53 cm of yarn. He used 21 cm. Peter now has 74 cm of yarn. --> **False** Cooper is 15 inches shorter than Bryce. If Cooper is 50 inches, then Bryce is 65 inches. --> **True**
9		8 inches 21 inches 100 meters
10		Jasmine needs to buy 2 more spools of thread. If she has 5 and each spool is 10 feet, then she already has 50 feet. She will need to buy 2 more, because one more will only be 60 feet and that still would not be enough.

Lesson 6: Represent Whole Numbers As Lengths On A Number Line

Question No.	Answer	Detailed Explanations
1	D	The answer is D. If you add 20 to 54, then you will get 74.
2	A	The answer is A. Each jump is 5. If you jump 5 times, then it is 20, 25, and 30.
3	B	The answer is B. Each jump is 2. 2 + 2 + 2 = 6, so that is 3 jumps to reach 28 (22 + 6).
4	A	The answer is A. Each jump is 10. 35 + 10 = 45, so you will jump one time from 35 to get to 45.
5	B	The answer is B. Each jump is 6. 6 five times is 30 and 12 + 30 = 42.
6	B	The answer is B. Each jump is four. If you add 3 to 21 four times you will get 33.
7	15	The answer is 15.
8		Row 1 --> 18 Row 2 --> 22
9		Row 1 --> 33 Row 2 --> 65
10		10 40 ⟵ ┼ ┼ ┼ ┼ ┼ ┼ ┼ ⟶ I know that the 4th line is 40 because if you start at ten and count by tens with each jump, when you get to the 4th vertical line you will say 40.

Lesson 7: Tell And Write Time From Clocks

Question No.	Answer	Detailed Explanations
1	D	The answer is D. The hour hand is on the six and the minute hand is on the 1, which represents :05.
2	A	The answer is A. The hour hand is on the eleven and the minute hand is on the 3, which represents :15.
3	C	The answer is C. The hour hand is in between the 8 and 9, and the minute hand is on the 6, which represents :30.
4	C	The answer is C. The hour hand is in between the 3 and the 4, and the minute hand is on the 9 which represents :45.
5	C	The answer is C. The time it is now is 12:15. In 5 minutes it will be 12:20.
6	D	The answer is D. The time it is now is 12:45. 15 minutes before it was 12:30.
7	3:30	Time is 3:30.
8		1st clock --> 1:45 2nd clock --> 4:15 3rd clock --> 6:30
9		1st clock --> 8:55 2nd clock --> 2:20 3rd clock --> 6:40
10		Kesha is correct. The time now is 11:20. 11:20 plus 5 minutes is 11:25.

Lesson 8: Solve Word Problems Involving Money

Question No.	Answer	Detailed Explanations
1	D	The answer is D. The value of a dime is 10 cent, so three dimes is 30 cents. The value of a penny is 1 cent, so 4 pennies is 4 cents. If you add them together, you get the total of $1.34.
2	A	The answer is A. The value of 2 quarters is 0.50, the value of 3 dimes is 0.30, the value of 4 nickels is 0.20, and the value of 1 penny is 0.01. If you add them together, you get the total of $1.01.
3	C	The answer is C. 3 dollars have a value of 3.00, 4 quarters have a value of 1.00, and 6 pennies have a value of 0.06. If you add them together you get $4.06.
4	B	The answer is B. 6 quarters have a value of 1.50, 3 dimes have a value of 0.30, and 2 nickels have a value of 0.10. If you add them together, you get $1.90.
5	C	The answer is C. Five dimes have a value of 0.50. One quarter have a value of 0.25 and one penny have a value of 0.01. If you add them together, you get $0.76.
6	A	The answer is A. The value of one dollar bill is 1.00, the value of four quarters is 1.00, the value of two nickels is 0.10, and the value of three pennies is 0.03. If you add them together you get $2.13.
7	$ 2.25	The answer is $ 2.25.
8		4 quarters, 1 penny, 2 dimes --> **$1.21** 2 dimes, 1 quarter, 10 pennies, 2 nickels --> **$0.65** 9 dimes, 2 pennies, 1 nickel, 2 quarters --> **$1.47**
9		2 dollars, 1 quarter, 6 nickels, 1 dime --> **$2.65** 5 dimes, 2 quarters, 3 nickels, 7 pennies --> **$1.22** 3 quarters, 1 dollar, 3 dimes, 2 nickels, 20 pennies --> **$2.35**
10		Bruce have enough money to buy the candy bar. If Bruce has 30 cent, 75 cent, and 55 cent, then he has the total amount of $1.60.

Lesson 9: Generate Measurement Data

Question No.	Answer	Detailed Explanations
1	C	The answer is C because on the line plot 4 and 6 does not have an x (any data plotted on that number).
2	A	The answer is A. Each x represents 2 pieces of ribbon.
3	C	The answer is C. Each x represent 2 pieces of ribbon. 4 Xs is 8 pieces of ribbon.
4	B	The answer is B. Each x counts for 2 pieces of ribbon. Kim has 4 pieces that is 3 inches, 4 pieces that are 5 inches, and 2 pieces that are 7 inches. There are 10 pieces of ribbon that are 3 inches or greater.
5	D	The answer is 10. Kim already has 4 pieces of 5 inch ribbon. If three more Xs were on the plot, that would represent 6 more 5 inch pieces of ribbon. 4 + 6 = 10.
6	A	The answer is A. There are 8 pieces of 1 inch ribbon and 2 pieces of 2 inch ribbon.
7	20	20 pieces of ribbon.
8		Kim has 4 more 1 inch ribbons than she has 3 inch ribbon. --> **True** Kim has 1 piece of ribbon that is 2 inches. --> **False** Kim has the same amount of 3 inch ribbon and 5 inch ribbon. --> **True**
9		If there were 3 Xs plotted on the 4, how many pieces of ribbon would Kim have that was 4 inches long? --> **6 pieces** If Kim uses all of her 3 inch ribbons and 1 of her 5 inch ribbons, how many pieces of ribbon did Kim use? --> **5 pieces**
10		Yes, Kim will have enough ribbon. Kim has 8 1-inch pieces already. She has 2 2-inch pieces. If she cuts each of the 2-inch pieces in half, she will have 4 1-inch pieces. 8 + 4 is 12.

Lesson 10: Draw Graphs To Represent Data

Question No.	Answer	Detailed Explanations
1	A	The answer is A. August only had 1 birthday.
2	D	The answer is D. The graph stops in between 2 and 4.
3	B	The answer is B. June has 10 birthdays.
4	B	The answer is B. There are currently 7 employees with December birthdays. If a new employee has a December birthday, then it will be 8 birthdays.
5	B	The answer is B. There are 2 people with a birthday in March and 1 person with a birthday in August. 2-1=1.
6	D	The answer is D. There are 3 birthdays in January and 4 birthdays in February. 3 + 4 = 7.
7	63	The answer is 63 employees.
8		The months with the most birthdays are May, June, and July. --> **False** There are 6 more people with a birthday in September than in August. --> **True** The same number of employees have birthdays in May and October. --> **True**
9		**July** month has 4 fewer birthdays than June. **January** month has the same number of birthdays as April. **February and November** TWO months have four birthdays.
10		There were 24 cupcakes ordered. 8 people have a birthday in May, 10 people have a birthday in June, and 6 people have a birthday in July. When you add them together that is a total of 24 cupcakes.

Chapter 4: Geometry

Lesson 1: Recognize And Draw Shapes

You can scan the QR code given below or use the url to access additional EdSearch resources including videos and mobile apps related to *Recognize And Draw Shapes*.

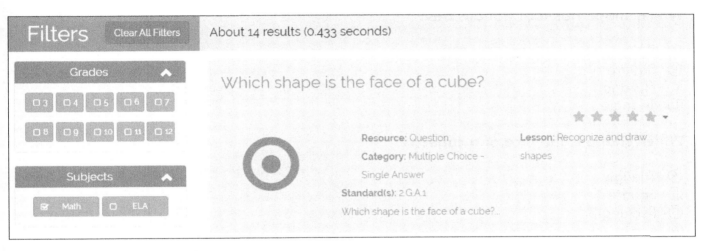

Recognize And Draw Shapes

URL	QR Code
http://www.lumoslearning.com/a/2ga1	

1. Which shape is shown below?

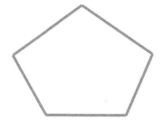

   Ⓐ Square
   Ⓑ Rhombus
   Ⓒ Rectangle
   Ⓓ Triangle

2. Which shape has four equal sides?

   Ⓐ Rectangle
   Ⓑ Square
   Ⓒ Hexagon
   Ⓓ Triangle

3. Which shape is the face of a cube?

   Ⓐ Triangle
   Ⓑ Square
   Ⓒ Rectangle
   Ⓓ Circle

4. Which shape is shown below?

   Ⓐ Triangle
   Ⓑ Hexagon
   Ⓒ Pentagon
   Ⓓ Octagon

5. Which shape has 8 sides?

- (A) Hexagon
- (B) Pentagon
- (C) Trapezoid
- (D) Octagon

6. Which shape below is a hexagon?

(A)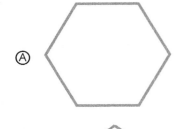

(B)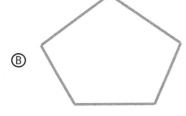

(C)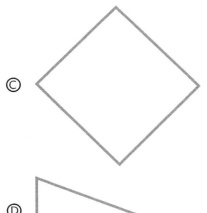

(D)

7. How many sides are in a quadrilateral?

8. Choose all of the correct attribute for the shape in each row.

	Has 6 sides	Has 4 sides	Has 5 sides
Hexagon			
Rhombus			
Pentagon			

9. Complete the table by filling in the missing column (Draw shapes).

Hexagon	
Rhombus	
Pentagon	
Triangle	

10. Draw a shape that: • Has four sides
                             • Is wider than it is longer
What shape did you draw? How did you know to draw that shape.

Chapter 4

Lesson 2: Partition a Rectangle Into Rows And Columns

You can scan the QR code given below or use the url to access additional EdSearch resources including videos and mobile apps related to *Partition a Rectangle Into Rows And Columns.*

 **Partition a Rectangle Into Rows And Columns**

URL	QR Code
http://www.lumoslearning.com/a/2ga2	

1. Which shape is portioned into 3 rows and 4 columns?

Ⓐ

Ⓑ

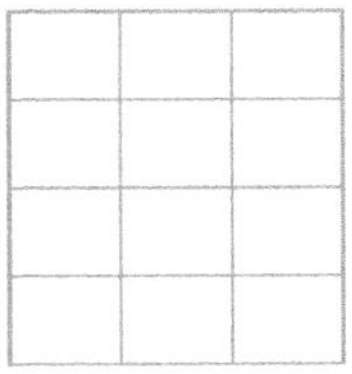

Ⓒ

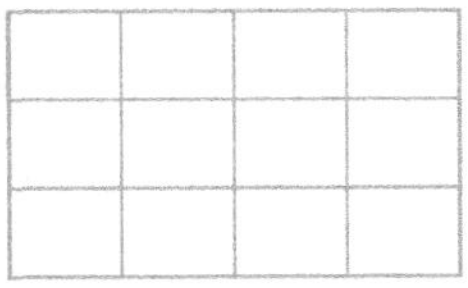

Ⓓ

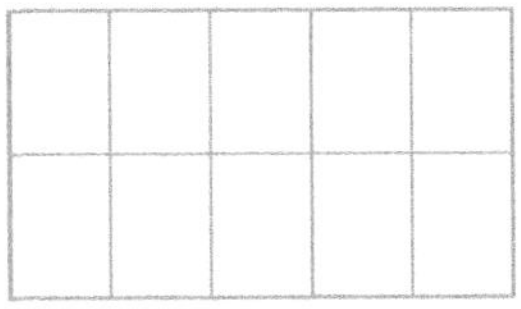

2. Which shape is portioned into 4 columns and 5 rows?

Ⓐ

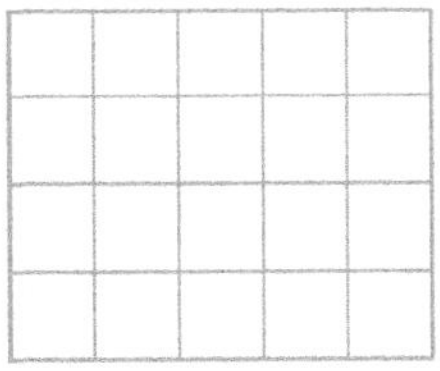

Ⓑ

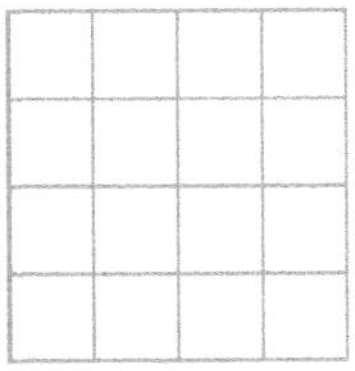

Ⓒ

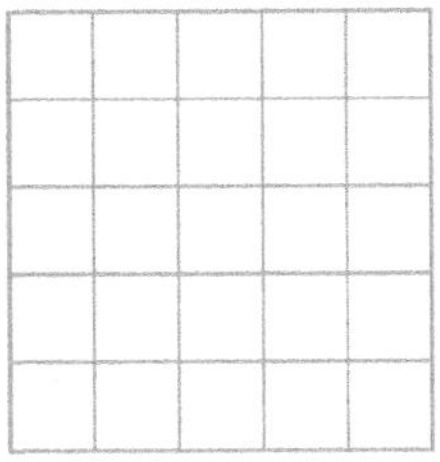

Ⓓ

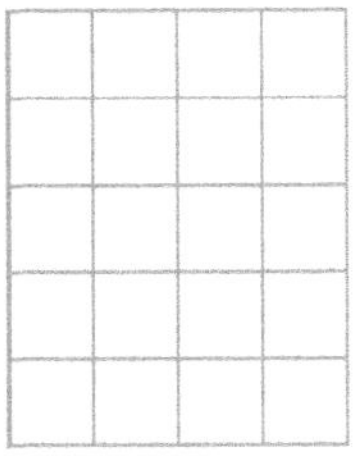

3. **How many rows and columns are in the shape below?**

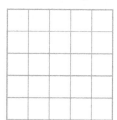

    Ⓐ 5 rows, 5 columns
    Ⓑ 4 rows, 5 columns
    Ⓒ 6 rows, 6 columns
    Ⓓ 4 columns, 5 rows

4. **How many rows and columns are in the shape below?**

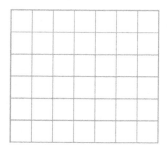

    Ⓐ 6 rows, 6 columns
    Ⓑ 7 rows, 6 columns
    Ⓒ 6 rows, 7 columns
    Ⓓ 7 rows, 7 columns

5. **How many squares are portioned into the shape below?**

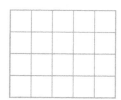

    Ⓐ 16
    Ⓑ 25
    Ⓒ 20
    Ⓓ 12

6. Which shape is portioned into 12 small squares?

Ⓐ

Ⓑ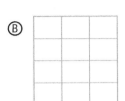

Ⓒ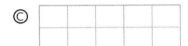

Ⓓ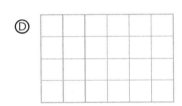

7. How many columns are in the shape below?

8. Complete the tables by matching each portioned shape to its total number of small squares.

	24	16	18

9. Complete the table by filling in the missing information in each column.

Shapes	Rows	Columns	Total Squares
	3		9
	4	3	
			35

10. Lucas and Josh are portioning a shape into 12 squares. Lucas made 6 rows and 2 columns. Josh made 4 rows and 3 columns. Who is correct? Draw each of their shapes below and explain your answer.

Name _____   Date _____

Chapter 4

Lesson 3: Partition Circles And Rectangles

You can scan the QR code given below or use the url to access additional EdSearch resources including videos and mobile apps related to *Partition Circles And Rectangles*.

 Search   ***Partition Circles And Rectangles***

URL	QR Code
http://www.lumoslearning.com/a/2ga3	

1. Which shape is portioned into two halves?

Ⓐ

Ⓑ

Ⓒ

2. Which shape is portioned into thirds?

Ⓐ

Ⓑ

Ⓒ

3. Which shape is portioned into fourths?

Ⓐ

Ⓑ

Ⓒ

4. What choice best describes the shaded part below?

Ⓐ One-Third
Ⓑ One-Fourth
Ⓒ One-Half

5. What choice best describes the shaded part below?

Ⓐ One-Fourth
Ⓑ Two-Third
Ⓒ Three-Fourths

6. Which choice best describes the shaded part below?

Ⓐ Two-Halves
Ⓑ One-Half
Ⓒ Two-Thirds

7. How many equal parts are in fourths?

8. Match each portioned shape with the choice that best describes it.

	Three-Fourths	Two-Thirds	Two-Fourths

9. Complete the table by filling in the column by naming the parts or drawing the parts.

	TWO-HALVES
	ONE-FOURTH

10. Brandon said that shape below is portioned into halves. Is Brandon correct? Explain your answer.

Chapter 4:

Geometry

Answer Key
&
Detailed Explanations

Lesson 1: Recognize And Draw Shapes

Question No.	Answer	Detailed Explanations
1	C	The answer is C. A rectangle has four sides.
2	B	The answer is B. A square has four equal sides.
3	B	The answer is B. The face of a cube is a square.
4	C	The answer is C. The pentagon has 5 sides.
5	D	The answer is D. An octagon has 8 sides.
6	A	The answer is A. A hexagon has 6 sides.
7	4	The answer is 4. Four sides are in a quadrilateral.
8		Hexagon --> **6** sides. Rhombus --> **4** sides. Pentagon --> **5** sides.
9		A Hexagon has 6 sides, Rhombus has 4 sides (All the sides of a rhombus are of equal length) and is diamond shaped, Pentagon has 5 sides, and Triangle has 3 sides.
10		I drew a rectangle. I knew to draw a rectangle instead of a square because a square has four sides equal. The shape I drew needed to be wider than it was longer.

Lesson 2: Partition a Rectangle Into Rows And Columns

Question No.	Answer	Detailed Explanations
1	C	The answer is C. Columns go up and down and rows go across. C has 4 columns and 3 rows.
2	D	The answer is D. Columns go up and down and rows go across. D has 5 rows and 4 columns.
3	A	The answer is A. Columns go up and down and rows go across. A has 5 rows and 5 columns.
4	C	The answer is C. Columns go up and down and rows go across. C has 7 columns and 6 rows.
5	C	The answer is C. The shape has 5 columns and 4 rows. If you count all of the small squares it is 20. If you add 5 + 5 + 5 + 5 or 4 + 4 + 4 + 4, the sum will be 20.
6	B	The answer is B. It has 3 columns and 4 rows. If you count all of the squares, you will count 12 squares.
7	2	The answer is 2 columns.
8		Row 1 --> 16 Row 2 --> 24 Row 3 --> 18

Question 9

Rows	Columns	Total Squares
3	**3**	9
4	3	**12**
7	**5**	35
2	**6**	**12**

Question 10

Lucas and Josh are both correct. If you count all of the squares in both of their shapes, they each have 12. You can also add 6 + 6 = 12. 3 + 3 + 3 +3 = 12.

Lesson 3: Partition Circles And Rectangles

Question No.	Answer	Detailed Explanations
1	C	The answer is C. Halves must be equal parts and C has two parts that are the same size.
2	A	The answer is A. Thirds must be equal parts and A has three parts that are the same size.
3	B	The answer is B. Fourths must be equal parts and B has four parts that are the same size.
4	A	The answer is A. There are three equal parts and one out of three parts are shaded.
5	C	The answer is C. There are four equal parts and three out of four parts are shaded.
6	A	The answer is A. There are two equal parts and two out of two parts are shaded.
7	4	Four equal parts are in fourths.
8		Row 1 --> TWO-FOURTHS Row 2 --> THREE-FOURTHS Row 3 --> TWO-THIRDS
9		
10	No	Brandon is not correct. There are two parts, but the parts are not equal so they are not half. If the shape was partioned into halves then each part would need to be the same size.

Additional Information

What if I buy more than one Lumos Study Program?

Step 1

Visit the URL and login to your account.
http://www.lumoslearning.com

Step 2

Click on 'My tedBooks' under the "Account" tab.
Place the Book Access Code and submit.

Step 3

To add the new book for a registered student, choose the ○ Existing Student button and select the student and submit.

To add the new book for a new student, choose the ○ Add New student button and complete the student registration.

Lumos StepUp® Mobile App FAQ For Students

What is the Lumos StepUp® App?

It is a FREE application you can download onto your Android Smartphones, tablets, iPhones, and iPads.

What are the Benefits of the StepUp® App?

This mobile application gives convenient access to Practice Tests, Common Core State Standards, Online Workbooks, and learning resources through your Smartphone and tablet computers.

- Eleven Technology enhanced question types in both MATH and ELA
- Sample questions for Arithmetic drills
- Standard specific sample questions
- Instant access to the Common Core State Standards
- Jokes and cartoons to make learning fun!

Do I Need the StepUp® App to Access Online Workbooks?

No, you can access Lumos StepUp® Online Workbooks through a personal computer. The StepUp® app simply enhances your learning experience and allows you to conveniently access StepUp® Online Workbooks and additional resources through your smart phone or tablet.

How can I Download the App?

Visit **lumoslearning.com/a/stepup-app** using your Smartphone or tablet and follow the instructions to download the app.

**QR Code
for Smartphone
Or Tablet Users**

Lumos StepUp® Mobile App FAQ
For Parents and Teachers

What is the Lumos StepUp® App?

It is a free app that teachers can use to easily access real-time student activity information as well as assign learning resources to students. Parents can also use it to easily access school-related information such as homework assigned by teachers and PTA meetings. It can be downloaded onto smart phones and tablets from popular App Stores.

What are the Benefits of the Lumos StepUp® App?

It provides convenient access to

- Standards aligned learning resources for your students
- An easy to use Dashboard
- Student progress reports
- Active and inactive students in your classroom
- Professional development information
- Educational Blogs

How can I Download the App?

Visit **lumoslearning.com/a/stepup-app** using your Smartphone or tablet and follow the instructions to download the app.

**QR Code
for Smartphone
Or Tablet Users**

Progress Chart

Standard	Lesson	Page No.	Practice		Mastered	Re-practice /Reteach
CCSS			Date	Score		
2.OA.A.1	Solve Addition And Subtraction Problems	5				
2.OA.B.2	Addition And Subtraction Problems	9				
2.OA.C.3	Groups Of Odd And Even Numbers	12				
2.OA.C.4	Addition Using Rectangular Arrays	15				
2.NBT.A.1	Three Digit Numbers	25				
2.NBT.A.1.B	Count In Hundreds	28				
2.NBT.A.2	Count Within 1000	34				
2.NBT.A.3	Read And Write Numbers To 1000 Using Base-ten Numerals	37				
2.NBT.A.4	Compare Two Three-digit Numbers	40				
2.NBT.B.5	Add And Subtract Within 100 Using Place Values	43				
2.NBT.B.6	Add Four Two-digit Numbers	46				
2.NBT.B.7	Add And Subtract Within 1000	49				
2.NBT.B.8	Mental Addition And Subtraction In Steps Of 10	52				
2.NBT.B.9	Explain Why Addition And Subtraction Strategies Work	55				
2.NBT.A.1.A	Bundle Of Tens	58				
2.MD.A.1	Measuring Length Of Objects	77				
2.MD.A.2	Measure Length Of Object Using Two Different Length Units	82				
2.MD.A.3	Estimate Lengths Using Different Units Of Measurement	86				
2.MD.A.4	Compare The Length Of Objects	89				
2.MD.B.5	Addition And Subtraction Word Problems Within 100	94				
2.MD.B.6	Represent Whole Numbers As Lengths On A Number Line	98				
2.MD.C.7	Tell And Write Time From Clocks	102				

Standard	Lesson	Page No.	Practice		Mastered	Re-practice /Reteach
CCSS			Date	Score		
2.MD.C.8	Solve Word Problems Involving Money	107				
2.MD.D.9	Generate Measurement Data	110				
2.MD.D.10	Draw Graphs To Represent Data	114				
2.G.A.1	Recognize And Draw Shapes	129				
2.G.A.2	Partition a Rectangle Into Rows And Columns	134				
2.G.A.3	Partition Circles And Rectangles	140				

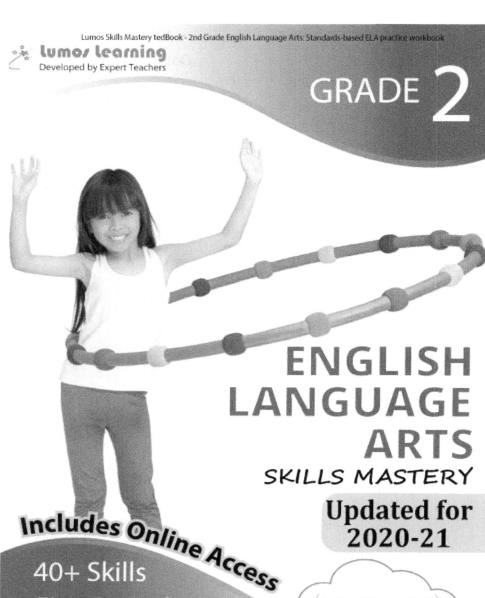

Lumos learning
Developed by Expert Teachers

GRADE 2

ENGLISH
LANGUAGE
ARTS
SKILLS MASTERY

Updated for
2020-21

Includes Online Access

40+ Skills
Five Strands

(((tedBook)))

Available
- At Leading book stores
- Online www.LumosLearning.com